PRENTICE HALL
MATHEMATICS STANDARDIZED TEST PREP

Elizabeth Marquez
Eileen Person

Needham, Massachusetts
Upper Saddle River, New Jersey

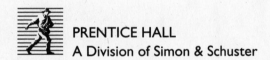

PRENTICE HALL
A Division of Simon & Schuster

Some of the material contained in this text has been reprinted from or based upon select versions of the Grade 11 High School Proficiency Test with the permission of the New Jersey Department of Education. This does not imply an endorsement by the New Jersey Department of Education.

ISBN: 0-13-839531-4

Printed in the United States of America

8 9 10 11 02 01 00

This book is dedicated to Chuck, Alison and Elizabeth.

About the Authors

Elizabeth Marquez

Liz Marquez teaches at North Brunswick Township High School in New Jersey. Her honors include the Presidential Award for Excellence in Mathematics Teaching and the Princeton University award for Distinguished Secondary School Teaching. She is an author of the New Jersey Standards for Teaching Mathematics and a consultant to the Educational Testing Service in the development of an assessment for national certification in mathematics teaching.

Eileen Person

Eileen Person is in her fifth year as the Supervisor of Mathematics for North Brunswick Township Schools. She was a distinguished teacher in the Presidential Scholars program and has served as a faculty consultant to the Educational Testing Service on the Advanced Placement Calculus Examination and on open-ended questions for the SAT I and II. As a member of the Academy Central SRA committee, she wrote sample SRA tasks. She is serving as President of the Lambda Chapter of the Delta Kappa Gamma Educational Society and is a member of Phi Delta Kappa.

Reviewers

We are grateful to our reviewers who provided helpful feedback and criticism throughout the development of this text.

Sheryl Bowie
Mathematics Instructor
Marysville Public Schools
Marysville, Michigan

Anita R. De Rosa
Supervisor of Mathematics
Jersey City Public Schools
Jersey City, New Jersey

Jerome D. Hayden
Mathematics Department Chairman, K-12
McLean County Unit District 5
Normal, Illinois

Joyce Krumtinger
Senior Consultant of Mathematics and Curriculum
Illinois State Board of Education
Normal, Illinois

James J. Mount
Mathematics Teacher
Southern Regional High School District
Manahawkin, New Jersey

Naser Neshiewat
Supervisor of Mathematics
Jersey City Public Schools
Jersey City, New Jersey

Ken Vineyard
Mathematics Instructor
Marysville Public Schools
Marysville, Michigan

Table of Contents

Introduction vii

Chapter 1: Patterns

1-1 Shape Patterns **1**

1-2 Identifying Positions in Patterns **4**

1-3 Two-Dimensional Patterns **7**

1-4 Sequences Based on Operations **11**

1-5 Sequences with Powers **14**

1-6 Primes, Factors, and Multiples **17**

1-7 Patterns in Tables **20**

1-8 Make a Table **24**

1-9 Scoring Open-Ended Questions **28**

1-10 Answering Open-Ended Questions **33**

Chapter Review **36**

Alternative Assessment Projects **40**

Chapter 2: Geometry and Measurement

2-1 Finding and Estimating Length **41**

2-2 Using Ratio and Proportion **46**

2-3 Triangles **50**

2-4 Quadrilaterals **54**

2-5 Circles **58**

2-6 Estimating Area **61**

2-7 Calculating Area **65**

2-8 Answering Open-Ended Questions **69**

Chapter Review **72**

Alternative Assessment Projects **76**

Chapter 3: Using Visual Aids

3-1 The Coordinate Plane **77**

3-2 Reflections and Translations **81**

3-3 Rotations **86**

3-4 Manipulating Shapes **89**

3-5 The Pythagorean Theorem **92**

3-6 Using a Diagram **96**

3-7 Fractals **100**

3-8 Three-Dimensional Figures **104**

3-9 Answering Open-Ended Questions **109**

Chapter Review **113**

Alternative Assessment Projects **116**

Chapter 4: Organizing and Using Data

4-1 Range, Mean, Mode, and Median **117**

4-2 Using Lists and Tables **121**

4-3 Bar Graphs **125**

4-4 Circle Graphs **129**

4-5 Probability **132**

4-6 Making Predictions **135**

4-7 Interpreting Graphs **138**

4-8 Choosing an Appropriate Graph **141**

4-9 Answering Open-Ended Questions **144**

Chapter Review **148**

Alternative Assessment Projects **152**

Chapter 5: Using Algebra

5-1   Evaluating Expressions   **153**

5-2   Variable Expressions   **156**

5-3   Equations and Formulas   **161**

5-4   Percents   **165**

5-5   More Percents   **170**

5-6   Solving Equations   **173**

5-7   Linear Equations   **178**

5-8   Answering Open-Ended Questions   **182**

Chapter Review   **186**

Alternative Assessment Projects   **190**

Sample Test 1   **193**

Sample Test 2   **203**

Sample Test 3   **211**

Sample Test 4   **219**

Sample Test Reference Page   **229**

Student Study Guide/Glossary   **231**

Acknowledgments   **246**

Introduction

The New Standardized Tests

Many states now require students to pass a standardized test in order to receive a high-school diploma. These new standardized tests are designed to help raise educational standards, to improve the quality of education, and to better prepare students to function as thinking members of society. The mathematics sections of these tests do not focus on computational skills: rather, they require that students apply those computational skills to problem-solving situations. The situations may call for students to apply several skills and their understanding of several concepts.

Mathematics Standardized Test Prep is designed to help students succeed on standardized tests. The focus is on improving problem solving through Patterns, Geometry and Measurement, Visual Aids, Organizing and Using Data, and Using Algebra. Students apply the strategies they've learned to answer the types of test questions they are likely to encounter: multiple choice, grid response, and open-ended.

The Lessons

Each lesson contains the following elements:

Work Together – This section consists of an activity (usually hands-on) that provides students the opportunity to share an exploration of a concept. This sharing promotes understanding of that concept and the ability to apply that concept.

Learn About It – This section is user-friendly and interactive. It keeps students involved by asking questions as a concept is being developed. In addition, these questions provide an ongoing assessment of students' understanding. When appropriate, this section may also contain one or more worked-out examples to provide students with a reference when they work on their own. Since many of the new standardized tests encourage the use of calculators, possible calculator key strokes are suggested for some computations.

Apply What You've Learned – This section allows students to solve problems independently and gauge their own understanding of the lesson concepts. The problems in this section also provide test-taking practice since they are in a multiple choice or free-response format.

Integrated Review – There are two multiple choice questions in this section: one that reviews a concept from the previous lesson and one that reviews a concept that may be from any lesson. With this spiral approach, every lesson is reviewed.

Open-Ended Problems

Open-ended problems require students to write clear, organized solutions to complex, multi-step problems. Students must explain how they arrive at their conclusions and may receive full or partial credit based on the quality of their response. Open-ended questions can be baffling to the students who are not sure of what is expected of them and to the teachers who may be at a loss for explanations for those students.

Each Chapter in *Mathematics Standardized Test Prep* ends with a lesson called Answering Open-Ended Questions. These lessons provide problems with sample answers that help students to understand how an open-ended problem is scored and how to improve their own answers using a scoring guide, or rubric.

Each Chapter Review includes an additional open-ended question for extra practice.

Alternative Assessment Projects

Some students simply do not perform well on tests. These students may better demonstrate their mastery through a performance-based project. At the end of each chapter in *Mathematics Standardized Test Prep*, there are two Alternative Assessment projects that provide another means of assessing students' knowledge of the chapter material. Each project includes a statement of the task and a scoring rubric for the teacher.

Test-Taking Simulations

At the end of the book there are four sample standardized tests. Each test consists of multiple choice questions, questions that provide no choices and require use of a grid for students' responses, and open-ended questions. Answer sheets are included for each test. These tests have suggested time limits and can provide opportunities to simulate test-taking conditions. The tests can be used diagnostically or for practice.

Student Study Guide/Glossary

This section at the end of the book provides definitions of terms used in the chapters and an example that illustrates each definition.

Absolute value (p. 77)	A number's distance from zero on the number line is called its absolute value.
Example	The absolute value of –3 is 3 because 3 is 3 units from zero on the number line.

Lesson 1-1: Shape Patterns

Learn About It

Patterns continue in predictable ways. Some patterns have a **repetend**, or a group of symbols that repeats.

Look at the pattern below.

▲✳✳☐☐☐▲✳✳☐☐☐▲✳✳☐☐☐▲✳

As you look at the pattern from left to right, you can see that the repetend is ▲✳✳☐☐☐.

1. a. Circle the three complete repetends that appear in the pattern.

  b. Underline any remaining shapes.

  c. Draw the next two shapes you would add to the underlined shapes to continue the pattern.

   ✳☐

Consider the following pattern.

✳✳◆◆◆☆☆☆✳✳◆◆◆☆☆☆

2. a. Circle the repetend.

  b. How many complete repetends appear? 2

  c. Draw the next two shapes that will continue the pattern.

   ◗✳

The pattern shown below has missing shapes within the pattern.

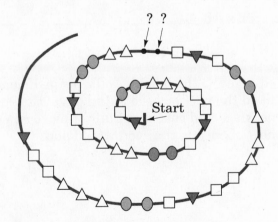

You can circle repetends to find missing shapes.

3. The repetend is ▼☐◯◯△△△☐☐

4. The missing shapes are △☐

Look at the pattern shown below.

This pattern does not have a repetend. Even though there is no group of symbols that repeats in exactly the same way, you can find a pattern.

5. Circle each group of symbols that begins with a star.

6. In the first three groups, the only change is in the number of telephone poles. Describe the pattern in the number of telephone poles in a group.

<u>In each group there is one more telephone pole than in the preceding</u>

<u>group.</u>

7. Use the pattern you found in Question 6 to draw the next three shapes in the pattern. (*Hint*: Complete the fourth group and begin the fifth group.) † ☆ ▭

Apply What You've Learned

Draw the next three symbols in each of the patterns below.

8. ◊ † † ∞ ◊ † † ∞ ◊ <u>† † ∞</u>

9. $ % ^ & * $ % ^ & * $ % ^ <u>& * $</u>

10. o o x x x o o o x x x o o o o x x x o o <u>o o o</u>

11. Π Σ ∂ Π Σ Σ ∂ Π Σ Σ Σ ∂ Π Σ <u>Σ Σ Σ</u>

12. Your friend Salim started to make this necklace for his girlfriend, but they broke up. You liked the necklace, so Salim gave it to you. You want to add to the necklace and continue Salim's pattern. On the necklace, draw the next six beads that you would add.

Add
here

13. Elizabeth made a mistake stringing beads. Look at her work, cross out the beads that must be removed to correct her error and draw an equal number of beads that will follow the pattern correctly.

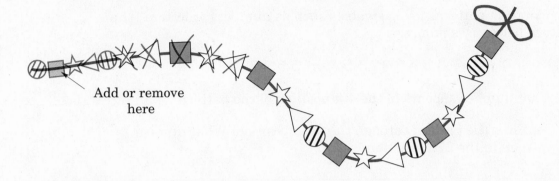

Add or remove here

14. Circle A, B, C, or D. Study the pattern below. Which choice gives the next five terms of this pattern?

§ § L § § LL § § LLL . . .

A. § LLL §   **B.** § § LLL   **C.** LLLL §   **D.** § LLLL

15. Circle A, B, C, or D. Which choice continues the pattern correctly?

X X O △ △ X X X O △ △ X X X X X O △ . . .

A. O X X X X   **B.** △ X X X X   **C.** X X X O △   **D.** X X X X O

Integrated Review

Circle A, B, C, or D.

16. The Robinsons measured each of their three children. Their heights were 4 ft 7 in., 4 ft 11 in., and 5 ft 3 in. What was the total of their children's heights?

A. 14.11 ft   **B.** 13.21 ft   **C.** 14 ft 9 in.   **D.** 14 ft 11 in.

17. Which of these is one way to find $\frac{3}{8}$ of a number?

A. Multiply the number by $\frac{8}{3}$.

B. Divide the number by 8 and multiply the result by 3.

C. Divide the number by 3 and multiply the result by 8.

D. Divide the number by 3 and divide the result by 8.

Lesson 1-2: Identifying Positions in Patterns

Learn About It

You can form patterns using symbols such as numbers or letters. The pattern below uses numbers.

$$1\ 3\ 5\ 7\ 9\ 1\ 3\ 5\ 7\ 9\ 1\ 3\ 5\ 7\ 9\ldots$$

1. What number appears in the 4th position of the pattern? <u>7</u>

2. Continue the pattern through the 27th position. What number appears in the 27th position?

<u>135791357913; 3</u>

3. Suppose you want to know the number in the 100th position. Do you think continuing the pattern would be a good method to use? Why or why not?

<u>Answers may vary. Sample: no; it would be too time</u>

<u>consuming.</u>

You can find the symbol in a certain position of a pattern by identifying the repetend. Then find the number of times the repetend appears in the pattern.

Example

Find the letter that is in the 71st position of the pattern.

$$T\ H\ I\ S\ I\ S\ E\ A\ S\ Y\ T\ H\ I\ S\ I\ S\ E\ A\ S\ Y\ldots$$

T H I S I S E A S Y   **Identify the repetend.**

T H I S I S E A S Y   **Assign a number to each position in the repetend.**
①②③④⑤⑥⑦⑧⑨⑩

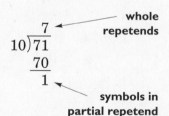

whole
repetends   **Divide the number of the position you want to find, 71, by the number of places in the repetend, 10.**

symbols in
partial repetend

If you continued the pattern through the 71st position, the repetend appears 7 times along with 1 more letter. This letter is the first letter of the next repetend, or T.

4. What letter is in the 73rd position? <u>I</u>

5. Suppose you are asked to find the letter in the 80th position.

   a. How many whole repetends would appear? <u>8</u>

   b. How many remaining letters would appear? <u>0</u>

   c. What letter is in the 80th position? <u>Y</u>

   d. Explain how you find which symbol appears in a position when you divide and the remainder is zero.

   <u>**Answers may vary. Sample: since there are no extra symbols, the**</u>

   <u>**last symbol in the pattern would be in that position.**</u>

6. What letter is in the 217th position? <u>E</u>

▮ Apply What You've Learned ▮

Use what you've learned about patterns to answer each question.

7. Suppose this pattern continues through the 94th position.

1 2 3 A B C 1 2 3 A B C . . .

   a. What symbol appears in the 94th position? <u>A</u>

   b. How many A's appear in the complete pattern? <u>16</u>

   c. How many odd numbers appear in the complete pattern?

   <u>32</u>

8. Deoxyribonucleic acid, DNA, can be thought of as a pattern which encodes genetic information. The pattern is made up of an arrangement of the four chemical bases listed below.

thymine (T)
guanine (G)
adenine (A)
cytosine (C)

The position and number of times these chemicals appear in the DNA pattern determine whether you are a person, dog, or a blade of grass. One possible arrangement of the chemical bases is shown below.

A T G T C A T G T C A T G T C . . .

   a. What base appears in the 45th position? <u>C</u>

   b. What base appears in the 3,000th position? <u>C</u>

9. A gold chain can hold 36 jewels. Can you make a necklace in which 2 rubies alternate with a pearl if you begin and end with a pearl? (*Hint*: Make a pattern by representing the pearls with the letter P and the rubies with the letter R.)

no

10. Find the decimal equivalent of $\frac{7}{11}$. What number is in the 77th position after the decimal point?

6

11. Find the decimal equivalent of $\frac{3}{7}$. What number is in the 83rd position after the decimal point?

7

12. **Circle A, B, C, or D.**   Which of the following will continue the pattern?

$$0.010110111\ldots$$

A. 0111011   **B.** 0111101

C. 1000010   **D.** 0110110

13. **Circle A, B, C, or D.**   A number that has a repetend after the decimal point is a *rational number*. A number that has a pattern but no repetend after the decimal point is an *irrational number*. Which one of the following is an irrational number?

A. 2.2 . . .   **B.** 2.020202 . . .

C. 2.121121112 . . .   **D.** 2.$\overline{078}$

Integrated Review

Circle A, B, C, or D.

14. Which of the following will continue the pattern?

▲ ▼ ▼ ▲ ▲ ▲ ▼ ▼ ▲ ▲ ▲ ▲ ▼ ▼ . . .

A. ▼ ▼ ▲ ▲ ▲   **B.** ▲ ▲ ▲ ▲ ▼

C. ▼ ▲ ▲ ▲ ▲   **D.** ▲ ▲ ▲ ▼ ▼

15. The repetend of a certain pattern is M M *G* A U M *G* M. What letter appears in the 103rd position?

A. M   **B.** *G*   **C.** A   **D.** U

Lesson 1-3: Two-Dimensional Patterns

Work Together

Some patterns consist of two-dimensional shapes. Work with a partner to look at the pattern of added tiles in the shapes shown below.

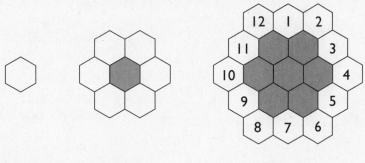

Shape 1   Shape 2   Shape 3

1. Use tiles to create Shape 4. If you do not have tiles available, use Shape 3, which is repeated below, as a base to draw Shape 4.

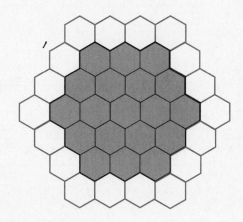

2. Complete the following table.

Shape Number	Number of Tiles
1	1
2	$1 + 6 = 7$
3	$1 + 6 + 12 = 19$
4	$1 + 6 + 12 + \underline{18} = \underline{37}$

3. Use the pattern in the table to predict the number of tiles you would add to each shape listed below in order to draw the next shape.

a. Shape 5 <u>24</u>   b. Shape 6 <u>30</u>

c. Shape 7 <u>36</u>   d. Shape 11 <u>60</u>

Learn About It

Recognizing a pattern in two-dimensional figures lets you predict information about the pattern without drawing all of the shapes. A table may help you recognize a pattern.

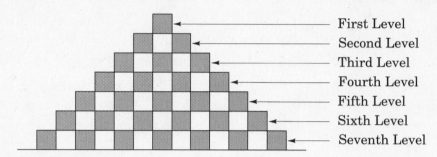

First Level
Second Level
Third Level
Fourth Level
Fifth Level
Sixth Level
Seventh Level

4. Complete the table.

Level	Number of White Squares	Number of Black Squares	Total Number of Squares
1	0	1	1
2	1	2	3
3	2	3	5
4	3	4	7
5	4	5	9
6	5	6	11
7	6	7	13

5. Use the patterns in the table to complete the following information for the 15th level.

   a. number of white squares **14**

   b. number of black squares **15**

   c. total number of squares **29**

You can generalize the patterns you found in the table by writing algebraic expressions. Let the nth level stand for any level of the table. The number of white squares on that level is $n - 1$ and the number of black squares on that level is n.

6. Write an algebraic expression for the total number of squares on the nth level. (*Hint*: Add the expressions for the number of white squares and the number of black squares.)

   $2n - 1$

The first five terms of a pattern are shown below. Each triangle is an equilateral triangle with sides of length one.

7. Complete the following table.

Term	Perimeter
1	3
2	4
3	5
4	6
5	7

8. Predict the perimeter of the 10th term. __12__

9. Write an expression for the perimeter of the nth term. __$n + 2$__

Apply What You've Learned

10. The first four terms of a pattern are pictured below. Each square has sides one unit long.

  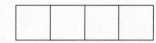

a. Complete the table below. Use the pattern in the table to predict the perimeter of the 12th term.

Term	Perimeter
1	4
2	6
3	8
4	10
5	12
. . .	. . .
12	26

b. Write an expression for the perimeter of the nth term. __$2n + 2$__

11. The following pattern is made up of black and white tiles.

1st Term   2nd Term   3rd Term

   a. The third term is repeated below. Use it as a base to draw the fourth term.

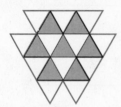

   b. Look for a pattern in the number of tiles added to each term. Predict the number of tiles that must be added to the fourth term in order to draw the fifth term.

12 tiles

12. The pattern shown below is made up of equilateral pentagons. The length of each side is one centimeter.

   Predict the perimeter of the fourteenth term. **44 cm**

Integrated Review

Circle A, B, C, or D.

13. Which of the following will best continue the pattern below?

###&&#$$###&&#$$###&&#$$#

   A. $$ **B.** #&   **C.** ##   **D.** &&

14. Find the decimal equivalent of $\frac{3}{7}$. What number is in the 17th position after the decimal point?

   A. 7   **B.** 1   **C.** 4   **D.** 2

Lesson 1-4: Sequences Based on Operations

Learn About It

A **sequence** is a set of numbers arranged according to a pattern. Some sequences of numbers are based on operations where you can add, subtract, multiply, or divide to go from one term to the next term.

Example 1

Find the next two terms of the sequence 33, 40, 47, 54, ...

To find the pattern, look at how the terms change.

$$33 \quad 40 \quad 47 \quad 54$$
$$+7 \quad +7 \quad +7$$

To find each term, you add 7 to the previous term.

$$54 + 7 = 61 \qquad 61 + 7 = 68$$

The next two terms are 61 and 68.

1. Find the next term of the sequence 134, 123, 112, 101, ...   <u>90</u>

In some sequences, the difference between terms changes.

Example 2

Find the next two terms of the sequence 20, 19, 17, 14, 10, ...

Again, look at how the terms change.

$$20 \quad 19 \quad 17 \quad 14 \quad 10$$
$$-1 \quad -2 \quad -3 \quad -4$$

The difference decreases by one with each pair of terms.

$$10 - 5 = 5 \qquad 5 - 6 = -1$$

The next two terms are 5 and -1.

2. Look at the sequence 5, 7, 11, 17, 25, ...

a. Describe how the terms change.

<u>The terms increase by consecutive even numbers.</u>

b. Use the pattern to find the next term of 5, 7, 11, 17, 25, ...

<u>35</u>

Example 3

Find the next two terms of the sequence $2000, 500, 125, \frac{125}{4}, \ldots$.

The terms of this sequence are decreasing in value. Subtracting, or adding a negative number, does not give you a pattern. Instead, look at dividing.

$$2000 \quad 500 \quad 125 \quad \frac{125}{4}$$
$$\div 4 \quad \div 4 \quad \div 4$$

To find each term, you divide the previous term by 4.

$$\frac{125}{4} \div 4 = \frac{125}{16} \qquad \frac{125}{16} \div 4 = \frac{125}{64}$$

The next two terms are $\frac{125}{16}$ and $\frac{125}{64}$.

3. Look at the sequence $3, 12, 48, 192, \ldots$.

   a. Describe what you would do to go from one term to the next term.

   Multiply by 4.

   b. Find the next two terms of this sequence. 768, 3072

You collect sports cards and you are interested in joining a club where you receive new cards every month. With Plan A you will receive 10 cards the first month, 20 cards the second month, 30 cards the third month and so on for 8 months. With Plan B you will receive 3 cards the first month, then the number of cards you receive will double every month for 7 more months. If both plans cost the same amount, which plan is the better buy?

4. To solve this problem, look at the number of cards you will receive.

   a. List the sequence of cards you will receive with Plan A.

   10, 20, 30, 40, 50, 60, 70, 80

   b. List the sequence of cards you will receive with Plan B.

   3, 6, 12, 24, 48, 96, 192, 384

   c. Which plan gives you more cards?

   Plan B

   d. If each plan lasted for only 6 months, which plan would be the better buy?

   Plan A

Find the next three terms in each of the following sequences.

5. 24, 27, 30, 33, . . . <u>36, 39, 42</u>

6. 814, 806, 798, 790, . . . <u>782, 774, 766</u>

7. 2, 6, 18, 54, . . . <u>162, 486, 1458</u>

8. −10, −9, −7, −4, . . . <u>0, 5, 11</u>

9. 5, 6, 9, 14, 21, . . . <u>30, 41, 54</u>

10. 600, 300, 150, . . . <u>$75, \frac{75}{2}, \frac{75}{4}$</u>

11. 75, 25, $\frac{25}{3}$, . . . <u>$\frac{25}{9}, \frac{25}{27}, \frac{25}{81}$</u>

12. Circle A, B, C, or D. Find the 7th term of the sequence 12, 7, 2, ...

    A. −8   **B.** −18   **C.** −13   **D.** −17

13. A dollar sign is usually drawn as an **S** with one or two vertical lines through it. As you can see at the right, if you draw one line, the **S** is divided into 4 parts and if you draw two lines, the **S** is divided into 7 parts. If you draw 8 lines, how many parts would the **S** be divided into? (*Hint*: Think of this as a sequence.)

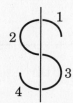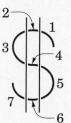

<u>25 parts</u>

Integrated Review

Circle A, B, C, or D.

14. A pattern is made up of hexagons. The perimeters of the first 4 terms are 6, 10, 14, and 18. Find the perimeter of the 6th term.

    A. 22   **B.** 36   **C.** 26   **D.** 30

15. A plumber charges $15 for coming to your home plus an additional $12 per half hour. What will the plumber's charge be if she is at your home for $2\frac{1}{2}$ hours?

    A. $60   **B.** $75   **C.** $30   **D.** $45

Lesson 1-5: Sequences with Powers

Learn About It

The expression 3^4 is called the fourth **power** of 3. In this expression, 3 is the **base** and 4 is the **exponent**. When the exponent is a counting number, it tells you the number of times the base is used as a factor.

$$3^4 = 3 \times 3 \times 3 \times 3 = 81$$

You can evaluate sequences using exponents. The first five terms of the sequence $2^1, 2^2, 2^3, \ldots$ are shown below.

$2^1 = 2$ $2^2 = 2 \times 2 = 4$ $2^3 = 2 \times 2 \times 2 = 8$

$2^4 = 2 \times 2 \times 2 \times 2 = 16$ $2^5 = 2 \times 2 \times 2 \times 2 \times 2 = 32$

Sequences can also involve zero and negative exponents. Consider the sequence $3^3, 3^2, 3^1, 3^0, 3^{-1}, 3^{-2}, \ldots$.

1. Find the value of the first three terms of the sequence.

a. $3^3 = $ <u>27</u>   **b.** $3^2 = $ <u>9</u>   **c.** $3^1 = $ <u>3</u>

2. To evaluate the sequence further, you need to look for a pattern. To go from one term of the sequence to the next term, what number do you divide by?

<u>3</u>

3. Find the value of the next three terms of the sequence by continuing to divide.

a. $3^0 = $ <u>1</u>   **b.** $3^{-1} = $ <u>$\frac{1}{3}$</u>   **c.** $3^{-2} = $ <u>$\frac{1}{9}$</u>

You used a pattern to evaluate zero and negative exponents. You can write the results of this pattern as a rule. If a is a nonzero number,

$$a^0 = 1 \quad \text{and} \quad a^{-n} = \frac{1}{a^n}$$

Example 1

Write the terms of the sequence 625, 125, 25, 5, . . . in exponential form. Then find the value of the next four terms.

You can write the sequence as $5^4, 5^3, 5^2, 5^1, \ldots$.

$5^0 = 5$ $5^{-1} = \frac{1}{5^1} = \frac{1}{5}$

$5^{-2} = \frac{1}{5^2} = \frac{1}{25}$ $5^{-3} = \frac{1}{5^3} = \frac{1}{125}$

Example 2

Find the units digit of 3^{27}.

You cannot answer this question by just using a calculator because the number is too large. Instead, look for a pattern.

	Value	Units Digit
3^1	3	3
3^2	9	9
3^3	27	7
3^4	81	1
3^5	243	3
3^6	729	9
3^7	2187	7
3^8	6561	1
3^9	19,683	3

The units digits of the powers of 3 form a pattern.

$$3, 9, 7, 1, 3, 9, 7, 1, 3, \ldots$$

The repetend is 3, 9, 7, 1. Remember, to solve this type of problem, you divide the position number by the length of the repetend. The length of the repetend is 4 and the position number is 27.

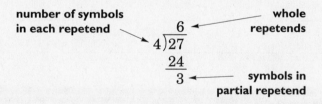

There will be 6 complete repetends and 3 terms from a partial repetend. The answer is 7, the third term of the repetend 3, 9, 7, 1.

4. Complete the following.

a. $7^1 =$ <u>7</u> $7^2 =$ <u>49</u> $7^3 =$ <u>343</u>

  $7^4 =$ <u>2,401</u> $7^5 =$ <u>16,807</u> $7^6 =$ <u>117,649</u>

  $7^7 =$ <u>823,543</u> $7^8 =$ <u>5,764,801</u> $7^9 =$ <u>40,353,607</u>

b. Use the pattern in part (a) to find the units digit of 7^{15}.

  <u>3</u>

Apply What You've Learned

Find the value of the first five terms of each of the following sequences.

5. $4^2, 4^3, 4^4, 4^5, \ldots$ <u>16, 64, 256, 1024, 4096</u>

6. $6^2, 6^1, 6^0, 6^{-1}, \ldots$ <u>36, 6, 1, $\frac{1}{6}$, $\frac{1}{36}$</u>

7. $25^{-2}, 25^{-1}, 25^0, \ldots$ <u>$\frac{1}{625}$, $\frac{1}{25}$, 1, 25, 625</u>

8. $10^{-1}, 10^{-2}, 10^{-3}, \ldots$ <u>$\frac{1}{10}$, $\frac{1}{100}$, $\frac{1}{1000}$, $\frac{1}{10,000}$, $\frac{1}{100,000}$</u>

9. Circle A, B, C, or D.   Find the 5th term of the sequence 9, 27, 81, ...

   A. 243   **B.** 1   **C.** 729   **D.** 2187

10. Circle A, B, C, or D.   Find the 6th term of the sequence 8, 4, 2, 1, ...

   A. -4 **B.** $\frac{1}{4}$ **C.** $\frac{1}{2}$ **D.** $\frac{1}{8}$

11. Circle A, B, C, or D.   Find the 5th term of the sequence 64, 8, 1, ...

   A. -8 **B.** -16 **C.** $\frac{1}{64}$ **D.** $\frac{1}{512}$

Find the units digit of each of the following.

12. 6^{21} <u>6</u>

13. 5^{55} <u>5</u>

14. 1^{100} <u>1</u>

15. 4^{32} <u>6</u>

Integrated Review

Circle A, B, C, or D.

16. Find the next two terms of the sequence 11, 7, 3, ...

   A. $-3, -7,$ **B.** $0, -3$ **C.** $-1, -5$ **D.** $1, 0$

17. You are organizing a school picnic. You want to buy enough juice boxes so that each of the 187 students will have one. If juice boxes are sold in cases containing 15 juice boxes, what is the smallest number of cases you can buy in order to have enough for the picnic?

   A. 13   **B.** 12.5   **C.** 12   **D.** 13.5

Lesson 1-6: Primes, Factors, and Multiples

Learn About It

A **prime number** is a number greater than 1 that is only divisible by 1 and itself. One number is a **factor** of a second number if it divides that number with no remainder.

Example 1

Is 6 a factor of 50?

One way to answer this question is to divide 50 by 6.

$$50 \div 6 = 8\frac{1}{3}.$$

Since 6 does not divide 50 evenly, 6 is not a factor of 50.

Another way to answer this question is to express 50 and 6 as products of their prime factors.

$$50 = 2 \cdot 5 \cdot 5 \qquad 6 = 2 \cdot 3$$

Since all of the prime factors of 6 are not also factors of 50, 50 is not divisible by 6.

1. Is 12 a factor of 76? Explain why or why not.

<u>Answers may vary. Sample: no; 12 does not divide 76 evenly.</u>

A **multiple** of a number is the product of that number and any nonzero whole number. The **least common multiple** of two or more numbers is the least number that is a multiple of each of the numbers.

Example 2

Find the least common multiple of 8 and 10.

The multiples of 8 are: 8, 16, 24, 32, 40, 48, ...

The multiples of 10 are: 10, 20, 30, 40, 50, 60, ...

The least common multiple of 8 and 10 is 40, the least number appearing on both lists.

2. Find the least common multiple of 15 and 40. <u>120</u>

You can use the least common multiple to help in solving problems.

Example 3

As music boxes come off an assembly line, Inspector A checks the 10th music box and every 10th one after that for the quality of the paint application. Inspector B checks the 25th music box and every 25th one after that for the quality of the gluing. Thus, a particular music box could be inspected twice. If 3,000 music boxes are produced in one day, how many of them are inspected twice?

Music boxes that are inspected twice are in positions that are multiples of both 10 and 25. The least common multiple of 10 and 25 is 50, so every 50th music box is inspected twice.

To find the number of multiples of 50 that occur in one day, divide 3,000 by 50.

$$3,000 \div 50 = 60$$

In one day, 60 music boxes are inspected twice.

Apply What You've Learned

3. A school van can accommodate 18 students.

   a. Find the greatest number of students it can carry in five trips.

   90 students

   b. How many trips are necessary to transport 47 students? **3 trips**

4. **Circle A, B, C, or D.** 18 is not a factor of 96 because

   A. 96 is not a prime number.

   B. 18 is not a prime number.

   C. 6 is not a factor of 96.

   D. 9 is not a factor of 96.

5. Carrie wants to purchase stamps from a machine. Stamps are $.29 each and the machine does not make change. Carrie has 7 quarters, 6 dimes, and 9 pennies.

   a. What should she deposit in the machine to get the maximum number of stamps without wasting any money?

   7 quarters, 5 dimes, and 7 pennies

   b. How many stamps will she get? **8 stamps**

6. Circle A, B, C, or D. On some days, a history teacher has the students in a particular class work in groups of 4, on other days in groups of 6 or 8. When all students are present, there is always one student left over after the groups are formed. Which of the following could be the number of students in that class?

   A. 37   **B.** 33   **C.** 29   **(D.)** 25

7. A refreshment stand buys hot dogs in packs of 36 and hot dog rolls in packs of 20. What is the least number of hot dogs and rolls that they can buy to have an equal number of each?

<u>**180 hot dogs and rolls**</u>

8. Circle A, B, C, or D. Joe ordered tables to be set up for the junior-senior prom; each of the available tables accommodated exactly 8 people. He knew that 251 people would come to the prom. He used his calculator to divide 251 by 8 and got 31.375. Therefore, he ordered 31 tables to be set up for the prom. His decision was

   A. good because he ordered just enough tables to accommodate everyone coming to the junior-senior prom.

   (B.) bad because he ordered too few tables to accommodate everyone coming to the junior-senior prom.

   C. bad because he ordered more tables than were needed.

   D. good because he allowed for some extra seating for chaperones.

9. On an auto assembly line, Irving checks the paint job on every 25th car. Elsa checks the brakes on every 20th car and Charlene checks the locks on every 50th car. If 450 cars come down the assembly line, how many will be checked for paint, brakes, and locks?

<u>**4 cars**</u>

Integrated Review

Circle A, B, C, or D.

10. What is the next term of the sequence 64, 16, 4, . . . ?

   (A.) 1   **B.** 0   **C.** −4   **D.** $\frac{1}{4}$

11. Which choice continues the pattern LLMLLMMLLMMMLL . . . ?

   (A.) MMMM   **B.** LMMM   **C.** LLMM   **D.** MMML

Lesson 1-7: Patterns in Tables

Learn About It

A relationship between two variables can be shown in a table of values or expressed by a rule.

1. In the table below, the relationship between x and y is given by the rule $y = x - 5$. Use this equation to complete the table.

x	y
3	−2
5	0
7	2
9	4
11	6

2. Complete the following table using the rule $b = 2a + 1$.

a	b
−4	−7
−2	3
0	1
2	5
4	9

Each of the relationships shown above is a *linear relationship*. A relationship between two variables, for example x and y, is a **linear relationship** if it can be written in the form $y = mx + b$ where m and b are real numbers.

Example 1

Which one of the following equations is *not* a linear relationship?

A. $y = -\frac{1}{3}x$ **B.** $d = c - 8$

C. $j = 2k + 7$ **D.** $b = \frac{1}{a}$

D is the only equation that is not a linear relationship because it involves division by a variable. **A** can be written $y = -\frac{1}{3}x + 0$, **B** can be written $d = 1c - 8$, and **C** is already in linear form.

You can find a rule for a table of values by looking at patterns.

Example 2

Write a rule for the linear relationship shown in the table. Then find the value of n, when $m = 10$.

m	n
1	−3
2	−6
3	−9
4	−12
. . .	. . .
10	

Look for a relationship between the numbers in the first column and the numbers in the second column. Each number in the second column is the number in the first column multiplied by −3. So, the rule for this relationship is $n = -3m$. When $m = 10$, $n = -3(10)$, or −30.

To find a missing value, you can use patterns in different ways.

Example 3

The table shows a linear relationship. Find the missing value.

c	d
1	1
3	5
5	9
7	13
9	

Each number in the second column is 1 less than the number in the first column multiplied by 2. So, the rule for this relationship is $d = 2c - 1$. The missing value is $d = 2(9) - 1$, or 17.

You can also find the missing value without finding the rule by looking at the pattern in each column. As each value in the c column increases by 2, each value in the d column increases by 4. So, the missing value is $d = 13 + 4$, or 17.

3. Think of a simple rule for a linear relationship and use that rule to fill in the first four values of k in the table. Then exchange work with your partner. Without knowing the rule your partner used, find the last value of k in you partner's table. Then, check your result with the rule your partner used.
Answers may vary. Check students' work.

j	k
0	
2	
4	
6	
8	

Apply What You've Learned

Complete each of the following tables using the equation given.

4. $y = 5x$

x	y
−2	−10
−1	−5
0	0
1	5

5. $m = 2n + 3$

n	m
0	3
−3	−3
6	15
9	21

Write a rule for each of the following linear relationships.

6.

a	b
4	−8
5	−10
6	−12
7	−14

$b = -2a$

7.

c	d
0	1
2	−1
4	−3
6	−5

$d = -c + 1$

8. Is $y = 2x^2 + 3$ a linear relationship? Explain why or why not.

Answers may vary. Sample: no; it involves squaring a variable.

9. Circle A, B, C, or D. The table below indicates a linear relationship.

x	y
1	−2
2	0
3	2
4	4
. . .	. . .
8	

What is the value of y when $x = 8$?

A. 6   **B.** 10   **C.** 14   **(D.)** 12

10. Circle A, B, C, or D. The table below indicates a linear relationship.

a	b
1	4
3	8
5	
7	16
9	20

Using the pattern in the table, what is the missing value of b?

(A.) 12   **B.** 10   **C.** 24   **D.** 18

Integrated Review

Circle A, B, C, or D.

11. What is the least common multiple of 6 and 15?

A. 3   **(B.)** 30   **C.** 60   **D.** 90

12. Which of the following numbers is a prime factor of 90?

A. 9   **B.** 10   **C.** 18   **(D.)** 2

Lesson 1-8: Make a Table

Work Together

When you fold a piece of paper in half repeatedly, how many sections will the folding produce? Is there a maximum number of times you can fold the paper? Work with a partner to find out.

When you fold a piece of paper in half and unfold it, there are two sections of paper as a result of your fold.

When you fold the paper for the second time, there are four sections.

1	2
3	4

Choose different types of paper. Work with your partner to fold the paper in half as many times as possible, then compare your results.

1. Use your data to complete the following table.

Number of Folds	Number of Sections
1	2
2	4
3	8
4	16
5	32
6	64

2. Circle A, B, C, or D.   Look for a pattern in your table. Which choice describes how to find the number of sections?

A. Multiply the number of folds by 2.

B. Add 2 to the previous number of sections.

C. Raise 2 to a power equal to the number of folds.

D. Square the number of folds.

3. If you could fold the paper 10 times, how many sections would you have?

__1,024 sections__

4. If you have 2^6 sections of paper, how many folds did you make?

__6 folds__

5. Circle A, B, C, or D. If n represents the number of folds, which expression represents the number of sections?

A. n^2 **B.** $2n$ **C.** 2^{n+1} **(D.)** 2^n

Learn About It

You can use a table to help you recognize a pattern. You can also use a table to solve problems involving time and money. To do this, fill in the table until you have reached the amount of money needed.

You want to hire a typist to type your term paper. He charges a base price of $25 and then charges $3 for each quarter hour of typing. The typist estimates that it will take one and three-quarter hours to type your paper. You have $40 to spend on typing. Can you afford to hire him?

6. Complete the table to show the cost of hiring the typist.

Typing Time	Quarter Hour Intervals	Cost in Dollars
0:00	0	25.00
0:15	1	25.00 + 3.00 = 28.00
0:30	2	25.00 + 6.00 = 31.00
0:45	3	25.00 + 9.00 = 34.00
1:00	4	**25.00 + 12.00 = 37.00**
1:15	5	**25.00 + 15.00 = 40.00**
1:30	6	**25.00 + 18.00 = 43.00**
1:45	7	**25.00 + 21.00 = 46.00**

7. Can you afford to hire the typist? Explain why or why not.

__Answers may vary. Sample: no; the typist will cost $46 and you__

__have saved only $40.__

Gordo's uncle told him, "I'll give you $50 if you can read 10 books by Thanksgiving. In fact, I'll pay you an additional $6 for the eleventh book, $7 for the twelfth book and so on." If Gordo reads 15 books by Thanksgiving, how much money will his uncle give him?

8. Complete the table to find how much money Gordo will receive.

Books Read	Dollars Received
10	50
11	50 + 6 = 56
12	50 + 6 + 7 = 63
13	50 + 6 + 7 + 8 = 71
14	50 + 6 + 7 + 8 + 9 = 80
15	50 + 6 + 7 + 8 + 9 + 10 = 90

If Abeba saves $150 a month and José saves $100 a month, in how many months will Abeba save exactly $1,000 more than José?

9. Complete the table showing the difference in savings.

Time in Months	Abeba's Money	José's Money	The Difference: Abeba's − José's
1	$150	$100	$50
2	$300	$200	$100
3	$450	$300	$150
4	$600	$400	$200
5	$750	$500	$250
6	$900	$600	$300

10. Completing the table does not answer the question, but it gives you enough information to see a pattern. Look at the even months.

   a. After 2 months, the difference is $100 .

   b. After 4 months, the difference is $200 .

   c. After 6 months, the difference is $300 .

11. In how many months will Abeba save $1,000 more than José?

   20 months

Apply What You've Learned

12. a. Complete the following table. Use the diagram to find the number of triangles you can draw from one vertex of each polygon.

Number of Sides	Number of Triangles
3	1
4	2
5	3
6	4
7	5
8	6
9	7

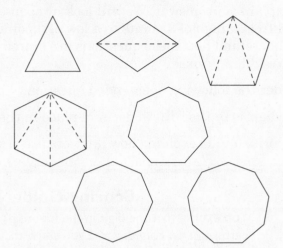

b. If a polygon has 100 sides, how many triangles can you draw? <u>98</u>

c. If a polygon has n sides, how many triangles can you draw? <u>$n - 2$</u>

13. On Tuesday, Josie rents a video from the library. She pays $1.50 for the first day's rental plus 50¢ per day for each extra day. What is Josie charged if she returns the video on the following Saturday?

<u>$3.00</u>

14. Each month, Ray puts $30 into a savings account and $18 into a checking account. By the time he has put $162 into his checking account, how much will he have put into his savings account?

<u>$270</u>

Integrated Review

Circle A, B, C, or D.

15. Find the value of the eighth term of the sequence $4^5, 4^4, 4^3, \ldots$

    A. -16 **B.** 0 **C.** $\frac{1}{64}$ **(D.)** $\frac{1}{16}$

16. The next term of the sequence $3, 4, 6, 9, 13, 18, \ldots$ is

    A. 5 **B.** 6 **(C.)** 24 **D.** 23

Lesson 1-9: Scoring Open-Ended Questions

Learn About It

When you answer an **open-ended question**, you must show your work and explain your answer. We will look at open-ended questions that are scored from a high of 3 points to a low of 0 points. It is important that you understand how these questions are scored so that you can give the best possible response.

Consider the following open-ended question.

What digit is in the fiftieth decimal place in the decimal form of $\frac{3}{11}$?

The scoring guide explains how answers are scored.

Scoring Guide

3   You explain that the digit in the fiftieth place is 7 based on a pattern or on counting and you show that the digits 2 and 7 alternate **or** you misread the word fiftieth as fifth or fifteenth, but follow this procedure and explain your work.

2   You identify the pattern of the digits 2 and 7 but you give a weak explanation or no explanation as to why 7 is in the fiftieth place **or** you convert $\frac{3}{11}$ incorrectly to 3.666. . . and explain why 6 is the digit in the fiftieth place.

1   You divide correctly (minor mistakes are O.K.), but you do not identify the digit **or** you identify 7 as the correct digit, but do not give an explanation or show any work.

0   You answer inappropriately or fail to attempt an answer.

Here are some sample student answers and their scores.

Sample 1

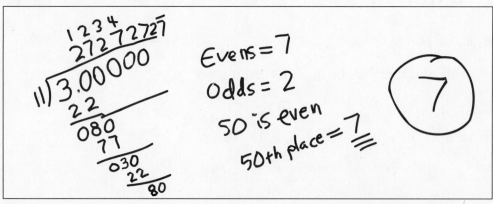

This response scores a **3**. It shows that 7 is in the fiftieth place, that 2 and 7 alternate, and it shows the pattern for the alternating digits.

Sample 2

.272727...
11⟌3.00000

BECAUSE odds = 2
AND EVENS = 7
AND 15 IS ODD
② IS THE ANSWER

This response scores a **3**. Notice that even though the answer is wrong, the response receives full credit. The student misread fiftieth as fifteenth, but gives a full explanation for the work.

Sample 3

$3.\overline{66}$
3⟌11.000

$3.\overline{66}$
3⟌11.0₂0

$\underline{6}$ because the digit 6 keeps repeating

This response scores a **2**. The student converts $\frac{3}{11}$ incorrectly, but provides some explanation of why 6 is the digit in the fiftieth place.

Sample 4

This response scores a **1**. Even though the answer is correct, the student does not show any work or give an explanation.

Work Together

Work together with a partner to score the following sample responses.
Use the scoring guide to explain your reasons for giving each score.
Then compare your answers with those of other groups. See if you can
agree on the scoring of each sample.

1.

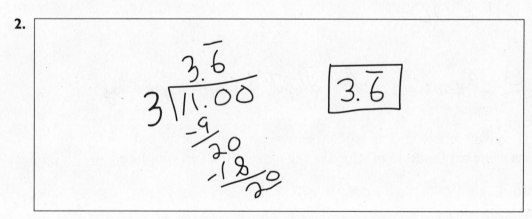

$$
11 \overline{\smash{)}\, 3.00000} \quad .27\overline{27}
$$
$$
\begin{array}{r}
-22 \\
\hline
80 \\
-77 \\
\hline
30 \\
-22 \\
\hline
50
\end{array}
$$

Number 7 will be in the fiftieth decimal place, because it is a repeating decimal.

Score **2** _____ Reasons **The student identifies the pattern but gives a weak explanation.**

2.

$$
3 \overline{\smash{)}\, 11.00} \quad 3.\overline{6}
$$
$$
\begin{array}{r}
-9 \\
20 \\
-18 \\
20
\end{array}
$$

$$\boxed{3.\overline{6}}$$

Score **1** _____ Reasons **The division is incorrect but the student recognizes 6 as the repeating digit.**

You want to put $2,000 into a bank so that your money can grow. The Happy Days Bank offers 0.25% monthly and The Safe Money Bank offers $2\frac{3}{4}$% yearly. Where should you deposit your money? Explain.

Scoring Guide

3 You choose the Happy Days Bank and explain why: either because $0.25 \times 12 > 2.75$ or you use the principal of $2,000 and calculate the amount of simple interest.

2 You state that Happy Days Bank is where to go since $3 > 2.75$ without explaining how you got 3.

1 You choose Happy Days Bank without sufficient explanation.

0 You answer inappropriately or fail to attempt an answer.

Score each sample response and explain your reasoning.
Answers may vary. Samples are given.

3.

> Happy Day's is better
> because 3% is better than 2.75%

Score **2**   Reasons **It states that 3% > 2.75%, but doesn't explain where 3% comes from.**

4.

> I would go to Happy Days Bank because they would compound .25% each month and Safe Money Bank will only compound .275 each year so it seem as if Happy Days Bank is better

Score **1**   Reasons **The choice is correct but the explanation is not sufficient.**

5.

Happy Days Bank
.25% month
.0025 month
.0025 × 12 = .03
is better

Safe Money Bank
2¾% yrly
.0275 yrly
.0275 × 1 = .0275

Happy Days is better because you have a .03 increase instead of .0275 like Safe Money Bank.

Score **3**   Reasons **It shows that 3% is the annual rate at Happy Days, which is greater than 2.75% at Safe Money.**

6.

You should deposit yor money in the Safe Money Bank because 2¾ is bigger than ¼ + your money will grow faster in the Safe Money Bank.
You get more money from SMB

Score **0**   Reasons **The answer is inappropriate.**

7.

You would deposit your Money at Happy Days Bank. If every month you get interest of .25% you will get $60 a year. If you get a compounding of 2¾% a year you only get $55 a year. It turns out that at the end of the year Happy Days Bank has the greater amount of interest
.0025 × 12 × 2000 = 60
.0275 × 1 × 2000 = 55

Score **3**   Reasons **The amount of interest at each bank has been correctly calculated and the work is shown.**

Lesson 1-10: Answering Open-Ended Questions

Work Together

You can work with a partner to improve your skills at answering open-ended questions. First work individually to answer the following question.

1. Estimate 97.85×209 in your head. Explain in writing what your estimate is and how you got it.
   Answers may vary. Check students' work.

2. The scoring guide shown below explains exactly how answers are scored. Exchange work with your partner and use the scoring guide to score each other's answer.

   Score: **Answers may vary. Check students' work.**

Scoring Guide

3 You clearly explain methods that can be done easily in your head (for example 100×200, 100×205, 100×209, 100×210, 90×200, 98×200) and your answer is consistent with the explanation.

or

You explain a more complex multiplication with some prerounding and no indication that the multiplication was not done in your head.

2 You round first but your computation does not match your explanation **or** you round and then add.

1 You round first but not enough to make computation easy and you give an explanation but no answer or you show your computation.

or

You give an estimate with no explanation.

0 You compute the exact answer then round **or** you give an incorrect response.

Here are two sample responses.

Sample 1

```
    209
   97.85
   ─────
    1045
   1672
   1463
  1881
 ──────────
 20450.65
```

My Answer is
20,451. I multiplied
209 times 97.85
(see work) and then
ESTIMATED

3. This response scored a **0**. Explain why. <u>Answers may vary. Sample: the</u> <u>exact answer was computed, not estimated.</u>

Sample 2

```
Estimate 97.85 & 209

   209
  X 98
  ─────
  1672           20,482
 1881
 ──────
 20,482
```

4. This response scored a **1**. Explain why. <u>Answers may vary. Sample: the</u> <u>rounding was not enough to make computation easy and the</u> <u>computation was shown.</u>

5. Look back at your answer to Question 1. If you did not score a **3**, use what you have learned to write an improved answer.
Answers may vary. Check students' work.

Apply What You've Learned

6. The Athletic Council wants to rent a hall for a sports banquet. They must pay $200 to rent the hall, plus $6 per person for food (not including tax).

   a. Which expense will not change no matter how many people come to the banquet? Explain your answer.

   b. The Council knows that at least 40 people, but not more than 80 people will come to the banquet. What are the least and greatest amounts of money the banquet could cost (not including tax)? Explain your answer.

SCORING GUIDE:

3   for (a), either fixed cost of $200 for the hall **OR** fixed $6 per person **AND** for (b), least cost $440 and greatest cost $680 **AND** adequate explanation.

2   computational flaws in (a) or (b), or inadequate explanation.

1   answers either (a) or (b) satisfactorily.

0   inappropriate answer or no answer

7. Use each of the digits 3, 4, 5, 6, 7, and 8 once and only once to form two three-digit numbers that will give the largest possible sum when they are added. Show your work.

   Is more than one answer possible? Explain your answer.

SCORING GUIDE:

3   makes a pair of 3-digit numbers with the sum 1,617 **AND** states that there is more than one possible pair with sum 1,617 **AND** explains 1,617 is the largest sum.

2   fulfills two of the three requirements above **OR** uses an incorrect operation (e.g. multiplication) and fulfills all requirements using that operation.

1   makes a pair of 3-digit numbers that do not have a sum of 1,617 **OR** repeats a digit, but finds the sum correctly **OR** repeats a digit and uses the incorrect operation.

0   inappropriate answer or no answer

Chapter Review

Circle A, B, C, or D.

1. Which of the following will continue the pattern below?

♥⇨✜○♥⇨⇨✜○♥⇨⇨⇨✜○♥⇨⇨⇨

    A. ✜○♥   **B.** ♥⇨✜

    C. ⇨⇨✜   **(D.)** ⇨✜○

2. Identify the letter in the 63rd position of the pattern:

SMOKINGISBADSMOKINGISBADSMOKINGISB . . .

    A. S   **B.** M   **(C.)** O   **D.** K

3. The first three terms of a tile pattern are shown below.

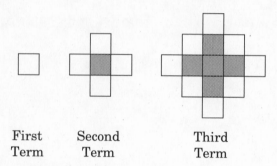

First   Second   Third
Term   Term   Term

How many tiles would you have to add to the fourth term in order to create the fifth term?

    A. 12   **(B.)** 16   **C.** 32   **D.** 41

4. Stan's grandfather gave him $2 on his tenth birthday, $4 on his eleventh birthday, and $8 on his twelfth birthday. Stan's grandfather says that this pattern determines that he will give Stan $14 on his 13th birthday. Stan says that this pattern determines that his grandfather will give him $16 on his 13th birthday. Stan's sister says that either amount could be correct because each follows a pattern which begins "2, 4, 8." Who is correct?

    A. Stan only   **B.** Stan's grandfather only

    (C.) Stan's sister   **D.** nobody

5. Consider the following pattern in which the exponents are integers.

$$2^3, 2^2, 2^1, \ldots$$

If this pattern continues, what is the value of the seventh term in the pattern?

    A. $\frac{1}{2}$ **(B.)** $\frac{1}{8}$ **C.** -6 **D.** -8

6. What is the units digit of the sixteenth term of the sequence below?

$$3^1, 3^2, 3^3, \ldots$$

(A.) 1   **B.** 3   **C.** 7   **D.** 9

7. A warehouse manager's computer showed that there were 382 baseballs in stock. The baseballs were all in full boxes of 4 or 12. The manager claimed the computer's count was wrong. The manager was correct because 382 is not divisible by

A. 3   **(B.)** 4   **C.** 6   **D.** 12

8. If a and b are whole numbers that satisfy the equation $5a + 8b = 100$, which of the following statements must be true?

A. b must be even.   **B.** b must be prime.

(C.) b must be a multiple of 5.   **D.** b must be divisible by 8.

9. The table below indicates a relationship between a and b.

a	b
0	−2
1	1
2	4
...	...
5	13
...	...
8	22

Which of the equations below expresses the relationship that is indicated in the table?

A. $b = a^2$ **B.** $b = 2a + 3$

(C.) $b = 3a - 2$ **D.** $b = a + 3$

10. Maggie and Keith are starting to save money for a car. Maggie saves $120 each month, and Keith saves $80 each month. At this rate, after how many months will Maggie have saved exactly $1000 more than Keith?

A. 5 months   **B.** 10 months

C. 20 months   **(D.)** 25 months

11. The table below indicates a linear relationship between a and b.

a	b
0	1
2	5
4	
6	13
8	17

According to the pattern, which of the following numbers belongs in the empty space in column b?

A. 7   **(B.)** 9   **C.** 10   **D.** 11

12. After clearing her calculator, Jody pushed the following keys on it in the order shown: 7 ✕ 1. After she pushed the = for the first time, she saw 7 on the display. Then, she repeatedly pushed only =.

After the second time she pushed =, she saw 49 on the display.

After the third time she pushed =, she saw 343 on the display.

After the fourth time she pushed =, she saw 2401 on the display.

After the 9th time Jody pushed =, what number appeared on her calculator display in the units (or ones) place?

A. 1   **B.** 3   **(C.)** 7   **D.** 9

13. A circular shape is cut from paper. If you fold the shape along a diameter, each section is $\frac{1}{2}$ of the original. If the resulting shape is folded in half along a radius, each section is $\frac{1}{4}$ of the original. If the original shape is folded in this manner a total of 5 times, the resulting sections are what fractional part of the original shape?

A. $\frac{1}{8}$ **B.** $\frac{1}{10}$ **C.** $\frac{1}{16}$ **(D.)** $\frac{1}{32}$

14. The fare for each taxi ride consists of a $3.00 initial charge and a charge of $1.20 per half-mile. At that rate, how much is the fare for a taxi ride of six miles?

A. $10.20   **(B.)** $17.40   **C.** $25.20   **D.** $32.40

Write your answer in the boxes at the top of the grid, one number (or decimal point) per box. Then fill in the correct circle below each box.

15. Find the eighth term of the following sequence: 310, 308, 304, 298, ...

2	5	4	

(Grid: column 1 filled at 2, column 2 filled at 5, column 3 filled at 4)

Answer the following open-ended question in the space below.

16. The triangular pattern of numbers below has some interesting characteristics. Except for the 1's, each number is the sum of the two numbers diagonally above it.

```
                    1                       Row 1
                1       1                   Row 2
            1       2       1               Row 3
        1       3       3       1           Row 4
    1       4       6       4       1       Row 5
  1     5     10      10      5      1       Row 6
 1    6    15    20    15     6     1        Row 7
1   7   21   35    35   21    7    1         Row 8
1  8  28   56   70   56   28   8   1         Row 9
```

What is the sum of the numbers in the 11th row? Show your work and explain how you found your answer.

SCORING GUIDE:

3   writes out rows 10 and 11 and adds the numbers in row 11 (1,204) OR sees the pattern of the sums of the rows (2^{n-1}) and computes $2^{10} = 1,024$.

2   incorrectly writes out row 11 but adds correctly OR incorrectly computes the sum based on the pattern.

1   lists row 11 without adding the terms OR mentions the pattern without computing the sum of row 11.

0   inappropriate answer or response

Alternative Assessment Projects

Here are some projects that will demonstrate your understanding of the topics in this chapter.

Project 1

Create a number pattern and a shape pattern. List the first four terms of each pattern, then write an explanation of how to continue each pattern.

SCORING GUIDE:

3   The student creates two patterns and gives an explanation of how to continue each.

2   The student creates one pattern and gives an explanation of how to continue or creates two patterns and shows some understanding of how to continue.

1   The student creates one pattern and shows some understanding of how to continue or creates two patterns without any explanation.

0   The student answers inappropriately or fails to attempt an answer.

Project 2

Make a poster that contains at least four photographs of real-world patterns. Show at least two different patterns. Write an explanation to accompany each pattern.

SCORING GUIDE:

3   The student's poster contains at least four paragraphs and two patterns, with a clear explanation of the patterns.

2   The student's poster shows four patterns that are similar with a clear explanation or shows two different patterns with minimal explanation.

1   The student's poster shows four similar patterns with a minimal explanation.

0   The student answers inappropriately or fails to attempt an answer.

Lesson 2-1: Finding and Estimating Length

Learn About It

Every position on a scale has exactly one *coordinate*. A **coordinate** is a number assigned to a point on a scale. To find the coordinate of a point on a scale, you must know the number of units in every subdivision.

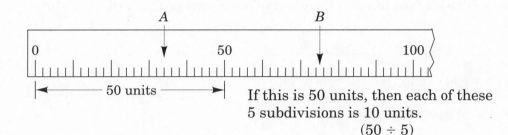

If this is 50 units, then each of these 5 subdivisions is 10 units.

$(50 \div 5)$

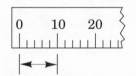

If this is 10 and there are 5 subdivisions, then each subdivision is 2 units.

$(10 \div 5)$

To find the coordinate of point *A*, count the number of larger (10 unit) subdivisions: 10, 20, 30. Now count the smaller (2 unit) subdivisions: 2, 4. So, coordinate A is $30 + 4 = 34$.

1. The coordinate of *B* is between __74 and 76_____.

Each of the largest subdivisions on the scale below is 1 cm.

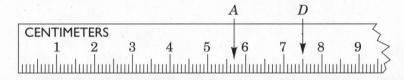

2. Each of the smallest subdivisions is 0.1 cm. Why? __Answers may vary.__
   __Sample: there are ten in each centimeter._____

3. How many complete large subdivisions are there from 0 to *A*? __5_____

4. How many smaller subdivisions are there between the last large subdivision you counted and *A*?

   __7_____

5. What is the coordinate of *A* on the centimeter scale? __5.7_____

6. Each of the smallest subdivisions on the ruler below is $\frac{1}{8}$ in. Why?

<u>Answers may vary. Sample: there are 8 to each inch.</u>

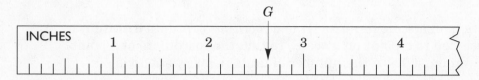

7. Use what you've learned in Questions 1–6 to find the coordinate of point G.

$2\frac{5}{8}$

8. Explain how you would find the coordinate of a point on any ruler. Once you have written your explanation, show it to a friend to find out if your explanation is clear.

<u>Answers may vary. Sample: find the sum of the number of larger</u>

<u>subdivisions up to the point and the number of smaller subdivisions.</u>

9. Measure each figure in inches and centimeters. Use the given points as guides for placing your ruler.

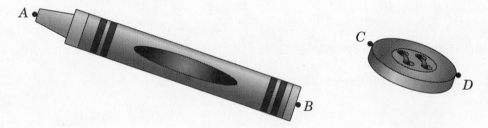

a. $AB = $ _$2\frac{7}{8}$_ in. or _7.4_ cm

b. $CD = $ _1_ in. or _2.5_ cm

c. $HG = $ _$1\frac{7}{8}$_ in. or _4.8_ cm

Sometimes it is useful to *estimate* length. To estimate length, you need to visualize the sizes of standard units. Look at a ruler that has both an inch scale and a centimeter scale. It shows that 12 in. is approximately 31 cm which means that one foot is about 31 centimeters.

Estimates may vary. Accept reasonable estimates.

10. Estimate the length of the following.

a. A toothbrush is about _7_ in. or _18_ cm.

b. Your teacher's height is about _____ ft or _____ cm.

c. The height of a 12-oz soda can is about _5_ in. or _12_ cm.

Compare a meter stick and a yard stick. Notice that 1 m is about 3 in. more than a yard. So, 39 inches is approximately equal to 1 meter.

11. Complete this statement with estimates.
The distance from the floor to the ceiling in your classroom is about

_____ ft or _____ m.   **Answers may vary.**

A kilometer is 1000 meters or a little more than a half of a mile. So, 2 kilometers is greater than one mile (or a little more than 20 city blocks).

12. Complete this statement with an estimate.

You go on a 30 km bicycle ride. You ride about __15__ mi.

13. Compare the estimates you wrote in Questions 10, 11, and 12 with those found by your classmates. Were your estimates too low, too high, or just about right?

Answers may vary. Check students' work.

Work Together

Work with a partner to estimate the measure of each item in metric units. Then measure each item.
Answers may vary. Check students' work.

Item	Estimated Measurement	Measurement
length of a paper clip		
width of this book		
height of a student desk		
length of the classroom		
width of the classroom		
length of the chalkboard		
width of the teacher's desk		

14. Compare your results with those of another pair of students. Explain why your measurements might not be exactly the same.

Answers may vary. Sample: different estimating methods may have been used.

Apply What You've Learned

Try Exercises 15–22 on your own. Then compare your answers with those of a friend.

15. Identify the coordinate of each point pictured below.

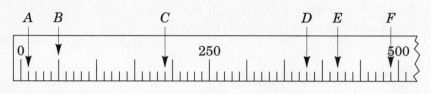

a. A <u>10</u>   **b.** B <u>50</u>   **c.** C <u>190</u>

d. D <u>380</u>   **e.** E <u>420</u>   **f.** F <u>490</u>

16. Identify the coordinate of each point pictured below.

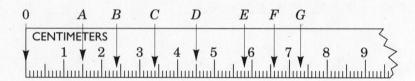

a. A: <u>1.5</u> cm or <u>15</u> mm

b. B: <u>2.4</u> cm or <u>24</u> mm

d. F: <u>6.6</u> cm or <u>66</u> mm

e. G: <u>7.3</u> cm or <u>73</u> mm

17. Identify the coordinate of each point pictured below.

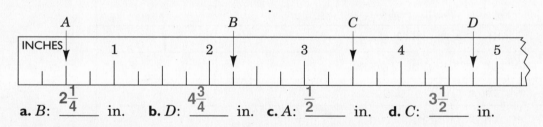

a. B: <u>$2\frac{1}{4}$</u> in. **b.** D: <u>$4\frac{3}{4}$</u> in. **c.** A: <u>$\frac{1}{2}$</u> in. **d.** C: <u>$3\frac{1}{2}$</u> in.

18. The length of the shaded shape is <u>3.8</u> cm or <u>38</u> mm.

---

19. Circle A, B, C, or D. The diameter of a quarter is about

    A. 12 mm   **B.** 3 m   **C.** 1 km   **(D.)** 2.2 cm

20. Circle A, B, C, or D. The distance between New York City and Los Angeles is about

    A. 30,000 cm   **B.** 100,000 mm

    (C.) 5,000 km   **D.** 50,000 m

21. Circle A, B, C, or D. The diameter of a full-sized automobile steering wheel is probably closest to

    A. 3.5 cm   **(B.)** 35 cm

    C. 350 cm   **D.** 3500 cm

22. Circle A, B, C, or D. You are out for a walk and come to a vast lake. A wise person sitting under a tree nearby tells you that the lake is 1.3 m deep, and then vanishes. What should you do to cross the lake?

    (A.) Wade across the lake.

    B. Build a raft.

    C. Make a running broad jump.

    D. Swim across and hope that you don't drown.

Integrated Review

Circle A, B, C, or D.

23. If the following pattern continues, what is the value of the seventh term in the pattern?

$$3^3, 3^2, 3^1, \ldots$$

    A. $\frac{1}{3}$ **B.** -3 **(C.)** $\frac{1}{27}$ **D.** 1

24. A repair company charges \$25 for a house call and \$30/h for labor. If t stands for the number of hours, which formula does the company use to determine a bill?

    A. $25t + 30$ **B.** $(25 + 30)t$

    C. $25 \div 30t$ **(D.)** $25 + 30t$

Lesson 2–2: Using Ratio and Proportion

Learn About It

Your friend Harry tells you that his father's new car can cruise at 15 miles per minute. Is Harry telling another one of his tall tales? One way to find out is to convert *miles per minute* into *miles per hour*. To do this, you need to understand what a ratio is and what a rate is.

A **ratio** is a comparison of two quantities. A ratio is usually expressed as a fraction. The ratio of the number of squares to the number of triangles in this design is $\frac{4}{10}$ or $\frac{2}{5}$.

1. What is the ratio of the number of triangles to the number of squares?

   $\frac{10}{4}$ or $\frac{5}{2}$

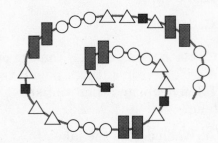

2. What is the ratio of the number of circles to the total number of figures?

   $\frac{12}{34}$ or $\frac{6}{17}$

A **rate** is a ratio that compares two different kinds of quantities. A rate of pay may be $5 per hour, or $\frac{\$5}{1\,h}$. A rate of speed may be 15 miles per minute, or $\frac{15\,mi}{1\,min}$.

Harry claims that the car travels at a rate of $\frac{15\,mi}{1\,min}$. Since you want the denominator in the rate to be 1 hour instead of 1 minute, multiply Harry's rate by $\frac{60\,min}{1\,h}$.

$$\frac{15\,mi}{1\,min} \times \frac{60\,min}{1\,h} = \frac{900\,mi}{1\,h} \text{ or } 900 \text{ mi/h}$$

3. Was Harry telling a tall tale? Explain.

   Yes; the rate is too fast for a car.

4. When you multiplied $\frac{15\,mi}{1\,min}$ by $\frac{60\,min}{1\,h}$, you did not change the value of Harry's rate because you actually multiplied by 1. Explain.

   1 h = 60 min, and $\frac{60\,min}{60\,min} = 1$

5. Suppose you want to convert $\frac{15\,mi}{1\,min}$ into a number of miles per second. Explain which multiplication you would use.

   $$\frac{15\,mi}{1\,min} \times \frac{60\,min}{3600\,s} \text{ or } \frac{15\,mi}{1\,min} \times \frac{3600\,s}{60\,min}$$

   Answers may vary. Sample: the first; it will give mi/s.

When two ratios are equal, you can write a *proportion*. When one of the terms of a proportion is a variable, you can use cross products to find the value of the variable.

Example 1

If 2 out of 10 high school students are licensed drivers, about how many students have licenses in a high school with 371 students?

$\dfrac{2}{10}$ **Write the ratio of high school students who are licensed drivers to all high school students.**

$\dfrac{d}{371}$ **Write a ratio for the school. Let d stand for the number of licensed drivers in the school.**

$\dfrac{2}{10} = \dfrac{d}{371}$ **Write a proportion.**

$10d = 2 \cdot 371$ **Write the cross products.**

$d = 74.2$ **Solve.**

There are about 74 licensed drivers in a high school of 371 students.

Drawing a picture may help you to decide what proportion to write.

Example 2

Water freezes at 0° Celsius (32° Fahrenheit) and boils at 100° Celsius (212° Fahrenheit). The thermometer on a building shows only the Celsius temperature. If that thermometer displays a reading of 14°C, what is the approximate temperature in degrees Fahrenheit?

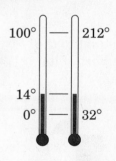

Sketch the two thermometers side by side, lining up the freezing and boiling points.

The difference between boiling and freezing on the Celsius scale is 100 − 0, or 100°.

The difference between boiling and freezing on the Fahrenheit scale is 212 − 32, or 180°.

$\dfrac{14}{100} = \dfrac{f}{180}$ **Write a proportion that compares the temperature to degrees between boiling and freezing points.**

$100f = 2520$ or $f = 25.2$ **Solve the proportion.**

Since $f \approx 25$, that means that the Fahrenheit temperature must be 25° *above* 32°, or 32 + 25, or 57°F.

Work with a partner on the following problem. You will need a centimeter ruler.

Lachanda lives at New Road and Fifth Street. She wants to walk to her friend Millie's house at Penny Lane and First Street. Lachanda wants to take the shortest route. How far must she walk if the scale on this map is 1 centimeter to 125 meters? (Make sure she doesn't walk through the school construction site. You don't want her to get hurt!)

1175 m

Map showing streets: 1st Street, 2nd Street, 3rd Street, 4th Street, 5th Street running horizontally. Vertical roads: River Road, New Road, Main Blvd., School Road, and Penny Lane (diagonal). Construction Site, No Trespassing area near 1st Street.

6. What proportion did you use to solve this problem? $\dfrac{1\ \text{cm}}{125\ \text{m}} = \dfrac{9.4\ \text{cm}}{x}$

Apply What You've Learned

7. Circle A, B, C, or D. The circles below have diameters equal to the diameter of the circle shown at the right. Each circle has part of its interior shaded. Which of the circles does *not* appear to have the same ratio of its interior shaded as the given circle?

A.   **B.**   Ⓒ.   **D.**

8. Circle A, B, C, or D. 1376 students attending Cary High School all voted for President of the Student Council. With approximately one-fifth of the votes counted, the leading candidate obtained 185 votes. Assuming that candidate obtained the same proportion of the total votes, about how many votes did she receive?

A. 275 **B.** 475 **C.** 475 Ⓓ.925

9. Circle A, B, C, or D. To solve a science problem, Luis has to convert 70 mi/h to an equivalent number of ft/s. Approximately which of these answers does he get when he performs the operations below?

$$\frac{70 \text{ miles}}{1 \text{ hour}} \times \frac{5280 \text{ feet}}{1 \text{ mile}} \times \frac{1 \text{ hour}}{60 \text{ minutes}} \times \frac{1 \text{ minute}}{60 \text{ seconds}}$$

A. 10 feet per second   **B.** 50 feet per second

(C.) 100 feet per second   **D.** 200 feet per second

10. Anyboro has a population of 28,000 people. In Anyboro, 3 out of every 14 people smoke. How many people do not smoke?

22,000 people

11. Suppose Lachanda's family has moved to River Road at 2nd Street. How many meters must Lachanda walk to get from her new home to Millie's home? Millie still lives on Penny Lane at First Street.

1037.5 m

Map showing 1st Street through 5th Street crossing River Road, New Road, Main Blvd., School Road, and Penny Lane, with a Construction Site (No Trespassing) near 1st Street. Scale: 1cm = 125m

Integrated Review

Circle A, B, C, or D.

12. On the scale shown below, the reading indicated by the arrow is between

Scale from 0 to 100 with arrow between 60 and 70.

A. 57 and 58   **B.** 60 and 62   **C.** 62 and 64   **(D.)** 64 and 66

13. 0.599×0.0212 is approximately

A. 0.12   **(B.)** 0.012   **C.** 0.0012   **D.** 0.00012

Lesson 2-3: Triangles

Learn About It

You can classify triangles by angle measures or by the number of sides that are congruent. Sides are *congruent* if they have the same length.

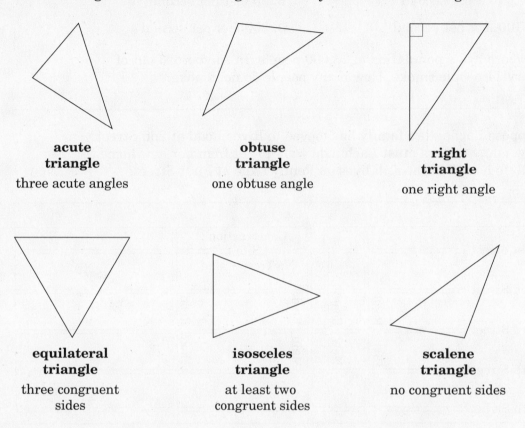

**acute
triangle**
three acute angles

**obtuse
triangle**
one obtuse angle

**right
triangle**
one right angle

**equilateral
triangle**
three congruent
sides

**isosceles
triangle**
at least two
congruent sides

**scalene
triangle**
no congruent sides

Draw a figure to fit each description. Use a ruler and protractor.
Compare your results with those of a friend.   1–4. **Check students' work.**

1. an isosceles right triangle

2. a scalene acute triangle

3. an isosceles obtuse triangle

4. a scalene right triangle

Congruent triangles have exactly the same shape and size. There is a correspondence between their vertices so that the corresponding sides and angles are congruent. The symbol ≅ means "is congruent to."

5. The two triangles below are congruent. Their corresponding congruent sides and angles are marked. Complete each statement.

a. ∠A ≅ _∠F_   b. ∠B ≅ _∠E_

c. ∠C ≅ _∠D_   d. $\overline{AB}$ ≅ _$\overline{FE}$_

e. $\overline{BC}$ ≅ _$\overline{ED}$_   f. $\overline{CA}$ ≅ _$\overline{DF}$_

g. △ABC ≅ _△FED_

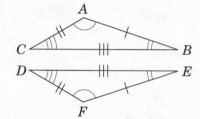

Similar triangles have the same shape but not necessarily the same size. When two triangles are similar, you can pair their vertices in such a way that the corresponding angles are congruent and the corresponding sides are in proportion.

6. △XYZ ~ △VMS. Use the diagram to complete each statement.

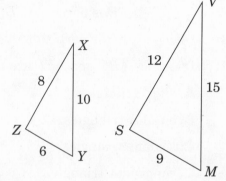

a. ∠X ≅ _∠V_

b. ∠Y ≅ _∠M_

c. ∠Z ≅ _∠S_

d. $\dfrac{XY}{VM} = \dfrac{YZ}{MS} = \dfrac{XZ}{VS}$

7. What is the ratio of each pair of corresponding sides of the similar triangles?
$\dfrac{2}{3}$

8. Can two similar triangles also be congruent? Explain.

   Yes; their corresponding angles are congruent and their corresponding sides are in the ratio 1:1.

Work Together

Work with a partner to draw the following on a separate sheet of paper. Use a ruler and protractor. Then compare your results with those of another pair of students. Make sure that you can justify your drawings.
9--11. Check students' work.

9. a pair of congruent obtuse triangles

10. a pair of congruent scalene triangles

11. a pair of similar triangles that are not congruent

12. Circle A, B, C, or D. Refer to the figure at the right. Triangle *ABC* is

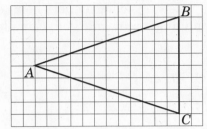

A. a right triangle.

B. an obtuse triangle.

C. an equilateral triangle.

(**D.**) an isosceles triangle.

13. Circle A, B, C, or D. Use the figure and the given information to answer this question. Assume that the figure shows distances and angle measures that are drawn as accurately as possible.

GIVEN: $\overline{BD}$ is parallel to $\overline{EG}$

$\overline{AE}$ is parallel to $\overline{DH}$

$\overline{AH}$ is perpendicular to $\overline{BD}$

Triangles *ABC* and *AEF* are **not**

A. right triangles.

B. similar triangles.

C. scalene triangles.

(**D.**) congruent triangles.

14. △*ABC* is equilateral. *D, E,* and *F* are the midpoints of the sides of △*ABC*.

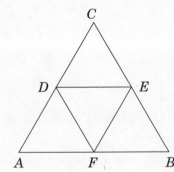

a. Identify all congruent triangles.

△*AFD,* △*FDE,* △*FBE,*

△*DEC*

Letters may be in any order.

b. Identify all similar triangles.

△*AFD,* △*FDE,* △*FBE,*

△*DEC,* △*ABC*

Letters may be in any order.

c. Identify one pair of triangles that are similar but not congruent.

Sample: △*AFD* and △*ABC*

15. Circle either TRUE or FALSE.

a. All isosceles right triangles are similar.

(TRUE)   FALSE

b. All equilateral triangles are congruent.

TRUE   (FALSE)

c. All equilateral triangles are similar.

(TRUE)   FALSE

16. Circle A, B, C, or D. Somewhere on this page, sketch two triangles that are similar but not congruent. Use your sketch to help you answer the following question. Which statement below is false?

(A.) The areas of the two triangles are equal.

B. The measures of the corresponding angles of the triangles are equal.

C. The measures of the corresponding sides of the triangles are proportional.

D. The perimeter of one triangle is greater than the perimeter of the other triangle.

Integrated Review

Circle A, B, C, or D.

17. Helmut sets up the conversion multiplication below. His starting units are meters per second. What are his ending units?

$$\frac{14 \text{ m}}{1 \text{ s}} \times \frac{60 \text{ s}}{1 \text{ min}} \times \frac{60 \text{ min}}{1 \text{ h}} \times \frac{1 \text{ km}}{1000 \text{ m}}$$

A. m per min   **(B.)** km per h

C. m per h   **D.** km per min

18. Susan bought ten yards of lace for $150 and her cousin Bridget bought 10 meters of the same lace for $150. Who got the better deal?

(A.) Bridget

B. Susan

C. Both deals were equally good.

D. There is not enough information to answer the question.

Lesson 2-4: Quadrilaterals

Work Together

Work with a partner. You will need an $8\frac{1}{2}$ by 11 in. sheet of paper, a ruler, and a protractor. When you have completed each activity, write yes or no in the table to indicate whether the quadrilateral always has the characteristic named in the first column.

Characteristic	Activity 1 Rectangle	Activity 2 Square	Activity 3 Parallelogram	Activity 4 Rhombus
Opposite sides parallel?	yes	yes	yes	yes
All four sides congruent?	no	yes	no	yes
Both pairs of opposite sides congruent?	yes	yes	yes	yes
All four angles congruent?	yes	yes	no	no
Opposite angles congruent?	yes	yes	yes	yes
Diagonals congruent?	yes	yes	no	no
Diagonals bisect each other?	yes	yes	yes	yes
Diagonals perpendicular?	no	yes	no	yes

Activity 1: The $8\frac{1}{2}$ by 11 in. sheet of paper is a *rectangle*. Examine and measure its sides, angles, and diagonals to discover its characteristics. The Activity 1 column for rectangles has been completed for you. (For example, since opposite sides are parallel, the word *yes* has been written in the table under Activity 1.)

Activity 2: Fold the paper so that a short side is on top of the long side. Fold the flap over to crease and mark it. Cut or tear off the flap. Unfold the paper and you should have a *square*.

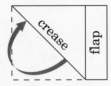 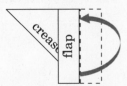 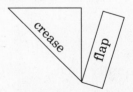 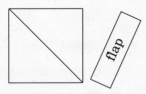

Examine and measure its sides, angles, and diagonals to discover the characteristics of a square. Write yes or no in each box to complete the column in the table under Activity 2.

Activity 3: Tear or cut the square along the diagonal. Slide triangle 1 to the left until the sides match as shown below. Tape them. You have a *parallelogram* without right angles.

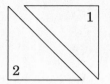 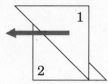 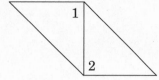

Examine and measure its sides, angles, and diagonals to discover the characteristics of the parallelogram. Write yes or no in each box to complete the column under Activity 3.

Activity 4: A *rhombus* is an equilateral parallelogram. Examine and measure its sides, angles, and diagonals to discover its characteristics. Write yes or no to complete boxes in the table.

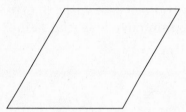

Compare your completed table with those of other pairs of students. Discuss any differences and decide on the correct answers.

Learn About It

Look at the pattern of yes and no responses for rectangles and squares in the table. Notice that all the yes answers for rectangles are also yes answers for squares. That means that squares have all the characteristics of rectangles, or that any square is also a rectangle.

1. Is a rectangle a parallelogram? Explain.

Yes; all yes answers for a parallelogram are also yes answers for a rectangle.

2. Is a rectangle a square? Why or why not?

No; a rectangle doesn't have four congruent sides.

3. Is a rhombus a square? Why or why not?

No; a rhombus doesn't have four congruent angles.

4. Is a square a parallelogram? Why or why not?

Yes; all yes answers for a parallelogram are also yes answers for a square.

5. Is a parallelogram a rhombus? Why or why not?

No; a parallelogram does not have four congruent sides.

Use a ruler and protractor to draw the quadrilaterals for Questions 6–8.
Refer to the table you completed to find the special names.

6–8. Check students' drawings.

    6. Draw a rhombus with all four angles congruent. Does this rhombus
       have a special name?   **yes**

      Special name? <u>square</u>

    7. Draw a parallelogram with congruent diagonals. Does this
      parallelogram have a special name?   **yes**

      Special name? <u>rectangle</u>

    8. Connect the endpoints of these segments and
      identify the type of quadrilateral that is
      formed.

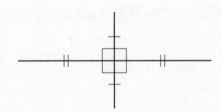

      Quadrilateral name? <u>rhombus</u>

Apply What You've Learned

    9. Circle A, B, C, or D.   Willie claims that every four-sided closed
      figure with all sides equal in length and with opposite sides parallel
      is a square. Which figure below can be used to prove that Willie is
      wrong?

    A.   **B.**   **C.**   **D.**

10. Circle A, B, C, or D. Which of the following is not a characteristic of all parallelograms?

A. Diagonals are perpendicular.

B. Diagonals bisect each other.

C. Opposite angles are equal.

D. Opposite sides are equal.

Answer yes or no to Exercises 11–13. Make sure you can justify your answers.

11. Is a rhombus a parallelogram? _yes_____

12. Is a parallelogram a square? _no_____

13. Is a square a rhombus? _yes_____

14. Circle A, B, C, or D. Which of these statements is TRUE?

A. All squares are similar.

B. All triangles are similar.

C. All rectangles are similar.

D. All parallelograms are similar.

15. Daniel says that all equilateral quadrilaterals are squares. In the space to the right, draw a figure to prove Daniel wrong.
Check students' drawing of a rhombus.

Integrated Review

Circle A, B, C, or D.

16. Which of these statements is TRUE?

A. Right triangles are always congruent.

B. Similar triangles are always congruent.

C. Congruent triangles are always similar.

D. Isosceles triangles are always equilateral.

17. Which list has the units of measurement arranged in order from LEAST to GREATEST?

A. quart, pint, gallon

B. pint, quart, gallon

C. pint, gallon, quart

D. quart, gallon, pint

Lesson 2-5: Circles

Learn About It

Three students started at the same flagpole in the middle of a large, flat grassy area and chose three different directions in which to walk. Each walked for 10 yards in a straight line away from the pole. Suppose many more students did this, each walking in a direction different from the direction chosen by each of the others. If you think of the final positions of the students as being points, which of the following figures would contain all of those points?

A. circle   **B.** square   **C.** rhombus   **D.** triangle

To solve this problem, use the strategy of drawing a diagram. Show points which represent the final positions of each of the three students. You may want to add more points for the additional students. You should realize that a *circle* is the figure that would contain the points. Recall that a **circle** is the set of points that are equidistant from a given point.

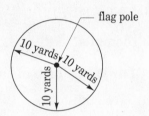

If you connected two students on opposite sides of the flagpole with a rope, the rope would represent a *diameter*. If you connected the flagpole to any student this rope would be a *radius*.

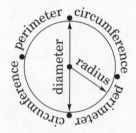

1. What is the diameter of the circle in the problem above? <u>20 yd</u>

2. What is the radius of the circle in the problem above? <u>10 yd</u>

The perimeter of a circle is called its *circumference*. You find the circumference, C, by using the formula $C = \pi d$ in which d represents the diameter of the circle, and π is the ratio of the circumference to the diameter. When you find a circumference with a calculator, you can use the π key. If you don't have a calculator, use 3.14 for the value of π.

3. What is the circumference of the circle in the problem above? <u>$\approx$ 62.8 yd</u>

Another formula for the circumference is $C = 2\pi r$ in which r represents the radius of the circle.

4. Why are the formulas $C = \pi d$ and $C = 2\pi r$ equivalent? <u>$d = 2r$</u>

You find the area of a circle by using the formula $A = \pi r^2$.

5. What is the area of the circle in the problem above? <u>$\approx$ 314 yd^2</u>

Work Together

Work with a partner on Questions 6–10. You will need a quarter, a piece of string, and a ruler.   **6–11. Answers may vary. Samples given.**

6. Wrap the piece of string around the edge of a quarter. Find the length of the string that fits perfectly around the circumference.

<u>7.8 cm</u>

7. Find the diameter of the quarter and use the formula to find the circumference.

<u>7.5 cm</u>

8. Compare your answers for Questions 6 and 7. If they are different, explain why. If they are not different, explain why they are the same.

<u>Sample: they are different because using the string is not as accurate</u>

<u>as measuring the diameter.</u>

9. Trace the quarter onto the centimeter grid at the right. Estimate the area by counting the number of squares plus fractional parts of squares within the circle.

<u>4 cm²</u>

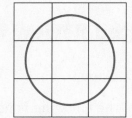

10. Use the formula to find the area of the surface of a quarter.

<u>4.5 cm²</u>

11. Compare your answers for Questions 9 and 10. If they are different, explain why. If they are not different, explain why they are the same.

<u>Sample: they are different because counting squares is less accurate</u>

<u>than measuring the radius.</u>

Apply What You've Learned

12. Circle A, B, C, or D.   Running Bear wants to visit Little White Dove who lives directly across Crater Lake. The lake is unusual because it is circular in shape. He knows that if he follows the circular path half way around the lake he will walk $1\frac{1}{2}$ mi. If he paddles his canoe across the lake, about how far will he travel?

    A. 3 mi   (**B.**) 1 mi   **C.** 9 mi   **D.** 2 mi

13. Your grandmother has a circular rug in her living room, and it needs new trim around its edge. Explain how you would determine how many yards of trim to buy.

<u>**Answers may vary. Sample: measure the circumference of the rug.**</u>

14. You work for a lawn care company and must fertilize a circular garden. On the package, it says that one container mixed with six gallons of water will cover 500 sq ft. If the diameter of the garden is 40 feet, how many containers of fertilizer will you need to do the job?

≈ 2.5 containers

15. You want to build a model of a tank that has 2" diameter wheels. The center of the wheels (axles) are 6" apart. How long must the track be to go around the wheels?

≈ 18.3 in.

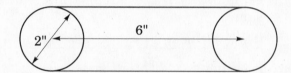

Integrated Review

Circle A, B, C, or D.

16. Which of the following is not a characteristic of all rhombi?

   A. Diagonals are perpendicular to each other.

   (B.) Diagonals are congruent to each other.

   C. All 4 sides are congruent.

   D. Opposite sides are parallel.

17. When Mr. Chavez does the family shopping, he keeps a running total of the prices of the items he puts in his shopping cart. The prices of the items in his cart are

$3.65 $11.98   43¢   43¢ $6.34 $2.99

$2.99   23¢ $2.23 $6.49 $2.78 $14.29

Estimate the total of the prices of those items. The total of the prices of those items is between

   A. $30 and $40   **B.** $40 and $50

   (C.) $50 and $60   **D.** $60 and $70

Lesson 2-6: Estimating Area

Learn About It

Suppose you had to estimate the area in square units of the shaded figure. In this figure, each completely shaded square has a dot.

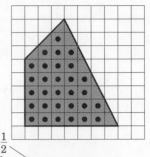

1. How many squares are completely shaded?

<u>30 squares</u>

You're not finished yet! You must now look at the squares that are partly shaded. Pair each square that is *more* than half shaded with a square that is *less* than half shaded. Each pairing has an area that is approximately equal to a shaded square. In this figure, a dot points to each pair that forms a complete square.

$\frac{1}{2}$
$\frac{1}{2}$
$\frac{1}{2}$

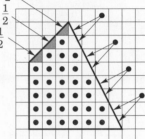

2. How many complete squares are formed by the pairing?

<u>4 squares</u>

3. There are three half squares that are not paired. What is the total area of these half squares?

$1\frac{1}{2}$ squares

4. Use your answers to Questions 1–3 to give an estimate of the total area of the figure.

$35\frac{1}{2}$ sq units

In the drawing of the lake, each square represents 4 square miles.

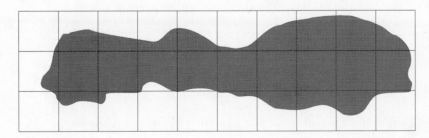

Answers may vary.

5. How many squares are filled or almost filled? <u>11</u>

6. How many squares are about half filled? <u>8</u>

7. Estimate the area of the lake. <u>64 mi^2</u>

You can also estimate area by counting rectangles. Read this problem and then answer Questions 8–15. Compare your answer to Question 15 with a friend. If your answers are different, go back and compare your answers for Questions 8–14.

Carla and her team have been given the problem of estimating the cost of carpeting their classroom. She suggests that they simply count the ceiling tiles to estimate the floor area. Below is a picture of their classroom ceiling. The shaded rectangles are lights. Each ceiling tile measures 48 in. by 24 in. If the replacement carpeting costs $11.99 per square yard, how much will it cost to carpet the room ?

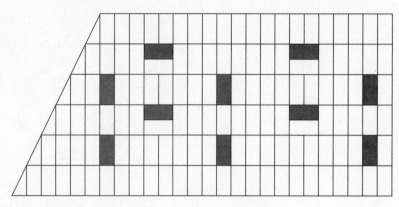

8. Find the area of one ceiling tile. Express your answer in square feet.

  8 ft^2

9. Should you find the area of the 10 rectangular lights? Why?

  Yes; there are no lights on the floor.

10. How many lights and whole rectangular tiles are there in the ceiling?

  135

11. What is the total area of the lights and rectangular ceiling tiles?

  1080 ft^2

12. How many tiles are half rectangles? What is their total area?

  6 tiles; 24 ft^2

13. Use your answers from Questions 11–12 to find the total floor area.

  1104 ft^2

14. Since a square yard measures 3 ft by 3 ft, 9 sq ft = 1 sq yd. Write and solve a proportion to find the number of square yards.

  $\frac{1104}{x} = \frac{9}{1}$; 122$\frac{2}{3}$ yd^2

15. What is the cost of carpeting the classroom? $1470.77

Sometimes, you can estimate area by using the strategy of making and labeling a drawing. When you label your drawing, make sure that you are consistent in the units of measure you use. In the following example, all the measurements are converted to inches.

Example

A roll of wrapping paper measures $2\frac{1}{2}$ feet by 2 yards. Jesse and his four sisters bought their mother a microwave oven for Mother's Day. The microwave box measures 28 in. by 19 in. by 15 in. Will one roll of wrapping paper be enough to wrap the box? Explain.

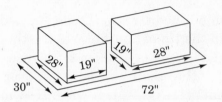

Make a sketch of how you can center the box on the wrapping paper.

There are two ways to center the box on the paper.

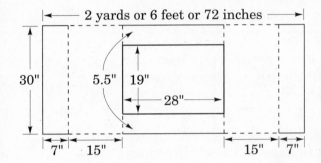

Make a detailed drawing of one of the ways to center the box on the paper.

Label the dimensions of the box and the paper and show how the paper could be folded to cover the sides.

In this case, 28 + 15 + 15, or 58 in. was used. That leaves 7 + 7, or 14 in., which is not enough to cover the top of the box.

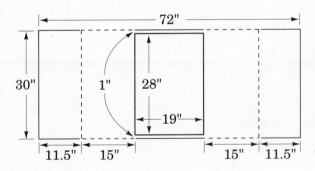

Make a detailed drawing of the other way to center the box on the paper.

Label the dimensions of the box and the paper and show how the paper could be folded to cover the sides.

In this case, 19 + 15 + 15 or 49 in. are used. That leaves 11.5 + 11.5, or 23 in. This is enough to cover the 19 in. across the top of the box. However, there is only 1 in. left on each of the other two sides which is not enough.

Neither placement of the box allows for enough paper to cover the box. Therefore, Jesse must buy more than one roll of wrapping paper.

16. Circle A, B, C, or D. Which of the following shaded figures has the same area as the shaded figure at the right?

A.    B.   C.   D.

17. Pratibha wants to put posters on her bedroom wall. She learned that her hand span, the distance from the tip of her pinky to the tip of her thumb when her fingers are spread open, is $6\frac{1}{2}$ inches. She uses her hands to approximate the width of the small wall near her door and counts 12 hand spans. The typical poster is $2\frac{1}{2}$ feet wide. How many posters will fit across Pratibha's wall?

<u>2 posters</u>

18. How many boxes that measure 10 cm by 10 cm by 40 cm can be wrapped with a 50.8 cm by 762 cm sheet of wrapping paper?

<u>19 boxes</u>

19. The manufacturer of a gallon can of paint says that it covers 500 square feet. The room you want to paint is 10 feet wide and 15 feet long. The walls are 8 feet high. You want to paint the ceiling and four walls. How many cans of paint should you buy?

<u>2 cans</u>

Integrated Review

Circle A, B, C, or D.

20. If you double the radius of a circle, its area

    A. doubles.   **B.** remains the same.

    C. is multiplied by 4.   **D.** is multiplied by $\frac{1}{2}$.

21. The scale on a map is $\frac{1}{2}$ in. = 20 mi. How far apart are two cities that are shown as being 5 in. apart on the map?

    A. 40 mi   **B.** 10 mi   **C.** 400 mi   **D.** 200 mi

Lesson 2-7: Calculating Area

Work Together

Work with a partner. This grid shows a triangle and a rectangle. Each figure has an area of 16 square units.

On the grid, draw as many different rectangles and triangles as you can that have an area of 16 square units. Use these formulas to check the areas of your drawings.

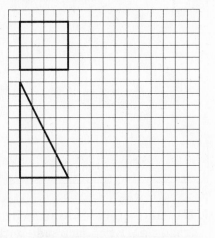

Rectangle: $A = lw$

Triangle: $A = \frac{1}{2}bh$

Compare results with another pair of students.
Check students' work.

Learn About It

Sometimes you need to calculate the area of a region that is neither rectangular nor triangular. In these cases, a good strategy is to break up the figure into triangles and rectangles.

The grid is composed of 100 unit squares. The shaded region has been broken up into a rectangle and two triangles.

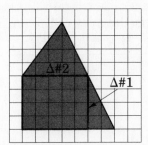

1. What is the area of the rectangle? (Use the formula $A = lw$.)

   20 sq units

2. What is the area of triangle I? (Use the formula $A = \frac{1}{2}bh$.)

   4 sq units

3. What is the area of triangle II? **10 sq units**

4. What is the area of the entire shaded region? **34 sq units**

This figure shows another way to break up the shaded region.

5. What is the area of the rectangle? **56 sq units**

6. How would you use this figure to find the area of the shaded figure?

   Subtract the areas of the two triangles from the

   area of the rectangle.

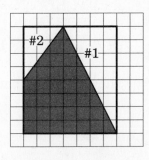

You can break up the figure below into one rectangle and one triangle. Use a ruler to do this.

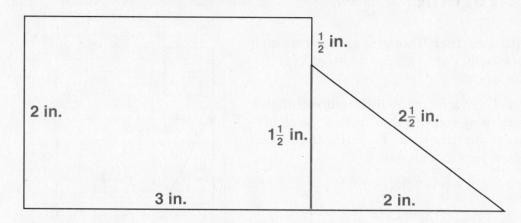

7. Use an inch ruler to measure the sides of the rectangle and the triangle. Label each side with the measurement you find.

8. Find the area in square inches of the rectangle. <u>6 in.²</u>

9. Find the area in square inches of the triangle. <u>$1\frac{1}{2}$ in.²</u>

10. What is the area of the entire figure? What is the perimeter?
<u>$7\frac{1}{2}$ in.²; 13 in.</u>

The concept of area can help you to solve everyday problems.

Example 1

Circle A, B, C, or D. Carpeting costs $12.00 per square yard. Using the floor plan, what is the cost of just enough carpeting to cover the entire floor of the den?

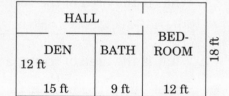

A. $180.00   **B.** $240.00

C. $864.00   **D.** $2160.00

$A = lw = 15 \cdot 12$ **Find the area of the den.**

$= 180$, or 180 ft^2

$\dfrac{180 \text{ ft}^2}{1} \cdot \dfrac{1 \text{ yd}^2}{9 \text{ ft}^2} = 20 \text{ yd}^2$ **Convert from square ft to square yd.**

$20 \text{ yd}^2 \cdot \dfrac{\$12}{\text{yd}^2} = \$240$ **Multiply the number of square yards by the cost per square yard.**

The cost for carpeting the den is $240.00. The correct answer is B.

You can use the strategies of making a drawing and using patterns to help you to solve certain problems involving area.

Example 2

A box can be covered with exactly 88 square inches of material. If a second box has dimensions exactly twice those of the first box, what is the least number of square inches of the same material which would cover it in the same way as the first one?

Sketch a box that is a cube with 1-in. edges. Each square face of the cube has an area of 1 in.^{2}. Since a cube has six congruent faces, it would take 6 square inches of material to cover it.

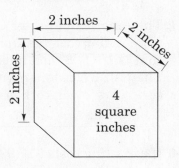

Next, sketch a cube whose dimensions are twice those of the first cube. Each edge of this cube is 2 in. Each square face of this cube has an area of 4 in.^{2}. The amount of material to cover this box would be 6 × 4 in.^{2}, or 24 in.^{2}.

If you double the dimensions of the cube with the 2-in. edges, each edge becomes 4 in. The area of each face is 16 in.^{2}, and the total amount of material needed to cover the box is 96 in.^{2}.

If you double the dimensions of the cube with the 4 in. edges, each edge is 8 in., the area of each face is 64 in.^{2}. The amount of material needed to cover this box is 384 in.^{2}.

Now look at the pattern of total areas:

$$6, \underset{\times 4}{} 24, \underset{\times 4}{} 96, \underset{\times 4}{} 384, \ldots$$

To find each term, you multiply the previous term by 4.

The least number square inches to cover the box in the problem is 4 × 88 or 352 square inches.

Apply What You've Learned

11. State three possible sets of dimensions, base and height, for a rectangle whose area is 24 square meters. Give an additional response that contains fractions.

   Answers may vary. Sample: 4 m × 6 m, 8 m × 3 m, 12 m × 2 m; $2\frac{1}{2}$ m × $9\frac{3}{5}$ m

12. Which of the following shaded figures has the same area as the shaded figure at right? Justify your answer by showing your calculations.

<u>They all do.</u>

$8(4) = 32$

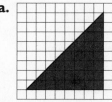

a.

b.

c.

d.

$\frac{1}{2}(8)(8) = 32$ $8(3) + \frac{1}{2}(8)(2) = 32$ $2\left(\frac{1}{2}\right)8(4) = 32$ $8 \cdot 4 = 32$

13. The American Coaster Company wants to cut circular coasters from a piece of cork that is 16" × 8" and have minimum waste. They cut 8 coasters from each sheet of cork. How much cork is wasted?

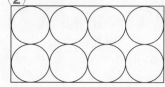

$\approx$ <u>27.5 in.^{2}</u>

14. If carpeting costs $16.99 a square yard, what is the cost of carpeting the bedroom in this floor plan?

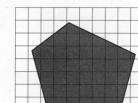

<u>$407.76</u>

Integrated Review

Circle A, B, C, or D.

15. Estimate the number of square units in the shaded figure.

A. 80 square units

B. 60 square units

C. 20 square units

D. 40 square units

16. As shown in the diagram, the picture is not centered on the wall from left to right. How far to the left should it be moved to be centered?

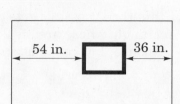

A. 9 in.

B. 18 in.

C. 27 in.

D. more information needed

Lesson 2-8: Answering Open-Ended Questions

Work Together

You can work with a partner to improve your skills at answering open-ended questions. First work individually to answer the following question.

1. Using a straightedge or ruler, draw two noncongruent rectangles each with a perimeter of 20 units. Indicate the length and width of each of your rectangles by writing the appropriate number of units next to the sides of each of them. Make your drawing on the grid to the right.
Check students' work.

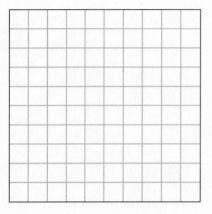

2. The scoring guide shown below explains exactly how answers are scored. Exchange work with your partner and use the scoring guide to score each other's answer.

Score: **Check students' work.**

Scoring Guide

3 You draw two noncongruent rectangles each with a perimeter of 20 units. If you fail to label the side lengths, the unit squares that make up the grid must correctly indicate the side lengths, or you may identify a scale that gives the correct side lengths.

2 You draw only one rectangle with a perimeter of 20 units.
or
You draw two noncongruent rectangles, neither of them with a perimeter of 20 units.

1 You draw one or more rectangles whose perimeters are not 20 units.
or
You draw two congruent rectangles whose perimeters are not 20 units.
or
You draw one or more non-rectangles with perimeters of 20 units.

0 You answer the question inappropriately or fail to attempt an answer.

Here are two sample responses.
Answers may vary. Samples are given.
Sample 1

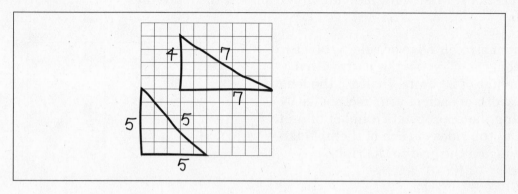

3. This response scored a **0**. Explain why. <u>**No rectangles were drawn and the**</u>
<u>**perimeters are not 20 units.**</u>

Sample 2

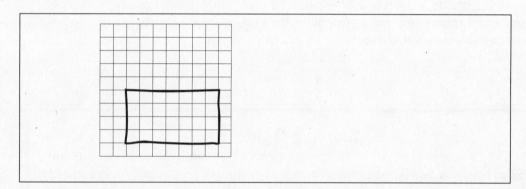

4. This response scored a **1**. Explain why. <u>**Only one rectangle was drawn,**</u>
<u>**and its perimeter is not 20 units.**</u>

5. Look back at your answer to Question 1. If you did not score a **3**, use
what you have learned to write an improved answer.
Check students' work.

7. Draw three quadrilaterals that are not similar and are not parallelograms.

SCORING GUIDE:

3   draws three different quadrilaterals that are not parallelograms (including squares and rectangles) **AND** are not similar

2   draws three quadrilaterals, none are similar but one is a parallelogram **OR** none are parallelograms but two are similar

1   draws three quadrilaterals, none are similar but all are parallelograms **OR** none are parallelograms but all are similar

0   inappropriate response **OR** no response

8. From collar to waist the length of Cindy's vest is 17 inches. She wants to add 4 buttons. Sketch the location of the buttons, if the buttons are to be equally spaced with one at the waist and one at the collar.

SCORING GUIDE:

3   places buttons correctly **AND** shows work

2   places buttons correctly but work is unclear **OR** buttons are placed incorrectly due to minor computational errors

1   places buttons correctly but work is missing **OR** buttons are placed incorrectly due to major computational errors

0   inappropriate response **OR** no response

Chapter Review

Circle A, B, C, or D.

1. The figure shows a circle of radius r inside a square of side length $2r$. In terms of r, what is the area of the shaded region inside the square and outside the circle?

   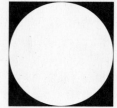

   A. $4r^2 - \pi r^2$

   B. $4 - \pi$

   C. $r^2 - \pi r^2$

   D. $4\pi r^2$

2. On the scale shown, the reading indicated by the arrow is between

   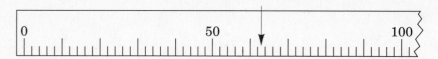

   A. 57 and 58

   B. 60 and 62

   C. 62 and 64

   D. 64 and 66

3. What is the ratio of the number of minutes in an hour to the number of minutes in a day?

   A. 60 to 24   **B.** 1 to 24   **C.** 60 to 1   **D.** 1 to 1

4. A typical walking rate is 1 mile in twenty minutes. If a jogger can jog about 3 times that speed, approximately how far would that jogger be able to jog in 2 hours?

   A. 2 to 3 miles   **B.** 5 to 6 miles

   C. 15 to 20 miles   **D.** 30 to 35 miles

5. The width of this page is closest to

   A. 20 kilometers   **B.** 20 decimeters

   C. 20 centimeters   **D.** 20 millimeters

6. In a neighborhood contest, each contestant threw a heavy weight three times. Ralph threw the weight 8 ft. 9 in., then 10 ft. 6 in., and then 11 ft. 2 in. What was the combined distance of Ralph's throws?

   A. 30.7 ft.   **B.** 29.17 ft.   **C.** 30 ft. 7 in.   **D.** 30 ft. 5 in.

7. Paula has an 8 inch by 16 inch picture which she glued onto a piece of matboard so that a 2-inch border of matboard was left showing all the way around her picture as indicated in the diagram. The cost of the matboard she used was $.02 per square inch. At this rate, what was the cost of the matboard indicated in the diagram?

A. $2.24

B. $2.56

C. $3.60

D. $4.80

8. A car traveled 4 miles in 6 minutes. What was its speed in miles per hour?

A. 1.5 miles per hour

B. 40 miles per hour

C. 60 miles per hour

D. 96 miles per hour

9. The Yourtown Preservation Society is campaigning for a law that would require the permission of the Yourtown Shade Tree Commission to cut down a tree that is more than 2 feet in diameter. They want to describe a 2 foot diameter tree by stating its circumference, a measurement found more easily by the everyday person. What would the circumference be for a tree that has a 2 foot diameter?

A. about 3.14 ft

B. about 1.57 ft

C. about 6.28 ft

D. about 4 ft

10. Howard drove his car 285 miles. It used $12\frac{1}{2}$ gallons of gasoline. How many miles per gallon did he get on the trip?

A. about 23 mi/gal

B. about 35 mi/gal

C. about 13 mi/gal

D. about 12 mi/gal

11. A baseball player's batting average is the ratio of the number of times he gets a hit to the total number of times he is at bat. During one season, a player got 75 hits and had a batting average of 0.300. What was the total number of times he was at bat for the season?

A. 225 times

B. 300 times

C. 250 times

D. 400 times

12. A certain high school reports that 6 out of 10 of its students have found summer jobs. What is the total student population of the high school if 522 students have found summer jobs?

A. 870   **B.** 780   **C.** 1044   **D.** 315

13. The scale on a map is 2 cm = 15 km. How far apart are two cities that are shown as being 7 cm apart on the map?

A. $52\frac{1}{2}$ cm   **B.** 30 km   **C.** $52\frac{1}{2}$ km   **D.** 105 km

14. A scale on a map is $\frac{1}{2}$ in. = 20 mi. How far apart are two cities that are shown as being 5 in. apart on the map?

A. 40 mi   **B.** 100 mi   **C.** 500 mi   **D.** 200 mi

15. A driver found that the distance from point A to point B by way of route 16 was approximately 45 miles. What would be the approximate driving distance between the same two points if the driver drove on the highway shown running directly through Metropolis?

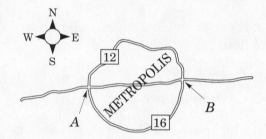

    A. about 15 miles

    B. about 30 miles

    C. about 45 miles

    D. about 90 miles

16. In order to attract new customers, the manager of a bicycle shop decided to hold a sale. A new bicycle regularly priced at $224 was placed on sale at 30% off that price. What was the sale price of that bicycle?

    A. $67.20

    B. $156.80

    C. $194.00

    D. $217.28

17. The block to the right is 2 inches by 2 inches by 2 inches and weighs 32 ounces. What would be the weight of a block of the same material that is 4 inches by 4 inches by 4 inches?

    A. 64 ounces   **B.** 96 ounces

    C. 256 ounces   **D.** 128 ounces

Write your answer in the boxes at the top of the grid, one number (or decimal point) per box. Then fill in the corresponding circle below each box.

18. For a cooked hot dog the ratio of the grams of saturated fat to the total gram weight is one to ten. How many grams of saturated fat are in one 125 gram cooked hot dog?

1	2	.	5

Answer the following open-ended question in the space below.

19. If a tree is cut down, you can see rings that represent its growth history. A new ring is formed each year as the tree gets larger. Rings vary in size because of such things as weather conditions, insects, and disease. If the largest redwood trees have a circumference of about 63 feet and an average ring size of 0.01 feet, about how old are these redwoods? Be sure to show all of your work and explain your answer.

SCORING GUIDE:

3   correctly uses the formula $C = 2\pi r$ to find the radius (10 ft), and finds the age of the tree to be 1,000 yrs **AND** work is clear

2   gives incorrect answer due to minor computational errors **OR** gives correct answer but work is unclear

1   gives incorrect answer due to major computational errors **OR** uses the incorrect formula **OR** gives correct answer but work is missing

0   inappropriate response or no response

Alternative Assessment Project

Here are some projects that will demonstrate your understanding of the topics in this chapter.

Project 1

Write a letter to a friend to help your friend identify and remember the properties of five different quadrilaterals.

SCORING GUIDE:

3   The student identifies five quadrilaterals **AND** states their properties correctly.

2   The student identifies five quadrilaterals **AND** states at least three properties correctly.

1   The student identifies five quadrilaterals but states less than three correctly **OR** identifies at least two quadrilaterals and states their properties correctly.

0   The student answers inappropriately **OR** fails to attempt an answer.

Project 2

Find several boxes of different sizes and shapes. Measure the dimensions of the boxes and explain how much wrapping paper will be needed to cover all of the boxes.

SCORING GUIDE:

3   The student gives the dimensions and answers correctly **AND** gives a clear explanation.

2   The student gives the dimensions but answers incorrectly due to a minor computational error **OR** student gives dimensions and correct answer but explanation is weak or unclear.

1   The student gives the dimension and correct answer but explanation is missing **OR** student gives dimensions but incorrect answer.

0   The student answers inappropriately or fails to attempt an answer.

Lesson 3-1: The Coordinate Plane

Learn About It

You can graph points on a number line. To **graph** a set of numbers means to locate the points named by those numbers on a number line. The number that corresponds to a point on a number line is called the coordinate of that point.

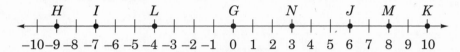

1. Use the number line above to name the coordinate of each point.

   a. H _−9_   **b.** N _3_   **c.** J _6_   **d.** G _0_

   e. Start at point J and move 3 units to the left. _3_____

The **absolute value** of a number is its distance from zero on a number line. Looking at 3 and −3 on the number line above, you can see that they both are 3 units from zero. The absolute value of 3 and −3 is 3. You write $|3| = 3$ and $|-3| = 3$.

2. Find each of the following.

   a. $|5|$ _5_   **b.** $|-8|$ _8_   **c.** $|-20|$ _20_   **d.** $|0|$ _0_

You can find the distance between two points on a number line by subtracting their coordinates. Actually, the distance between two points is the absolute value of the difference of their coordinates.

Example 1

Find the distance between point A and point B.

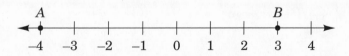

To find the distance between point A and point B, subtract the coordinates of the points. When you use absolute value, the order in which you subtract coordinates doesn't matter.

$$|3 - (-4)| = |3 + 4| = |7| = 7$$

or

$$|-4 - 3| = |-4 + -3| = |-7| = 7$$

The distance between point A and point B is 7.

3. The given numbers are the coordinates of two points on a number line. Find the distance between the points.

a. -2 and 6 __8__   b. 2 and 6 __4__

c. -8 and 1 __9__   d. -4 and -7 __3__

You use an **ordered pair** of numbers to locate a point on a **coordinate plane**. The first number in an ordered pair is the x-coordinate. The second number is the y-coordinate. A general way to locate a point is by naming the *quadrant* that a point is in. The quadrants are numbered as shown below.

The ordered pair $(-4, 2)$ has an x-coordinate of -4 and a y-coordinate of 2.

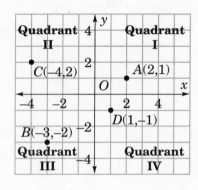

The coordinates of point D are $(1, -1)$. Point D is located in quadrant IV.

4. In which quadrant(s) do the x-coordinate and the y-coordinate of a point have different signs?

__II, IV__

You can represent geometric figures on a coordinate plane.

Example 2

Points $A(2, -1)$, $B(5, -1)$, and $C(2, 3)$ are the vertices of a right triangle. Plot the points on a coordinate plane and then find the area of $\triangle ABC$.

To find the area of $\triangle ABC$, you can use $A = \frac{1}{2}(\text{base})(\text{height})$.

Find the length of $\overline{AB}$.

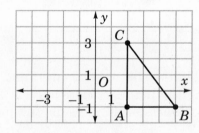

$$|5 - 2| = 3 \qquad \textbf{base}$$

Find the length of $\overline{AC}$.

$$|3 - (-1)| = 4 \qquad \textbf{height}$$

$$A = \tfrac{1}{2}(\text{base})(\text{height}) = \tfrac{1}{2}(3)(4) = 6$$

The area of $\triangle ABC$ is 6 square units.

Apply What You've Learned

5. You are playing a game in which you move a chip on a number line. Where you move the chip is determined by the cards you draw from a deck. Each card has an integer printed on it. On each turn, you move your chip to the location with the coordinate equal to the sum of the coordinate of your current location and the number on the card you draw.

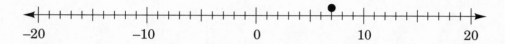

Your chip is now at the position shown above. For your next five turns, you draw cards with the following sequence of numbers: -2, 6, -7, -12, -4. What is the coordinate of the location of your chip after you complete this sequence of moves?

<u>−12</u>

6. **Circle A, B, C, or D.** In which quadrant(s) are both coordinates of a point negative?

   A. quadrant I **B.** quadrant II **C.** quadrant III **D.** quadrant IV

7. Write the ordered pairs for the vertices of the figure shown at the right.

   <u>(0, 3), (5, −2), (2, −2), (2, −5),</u>

   <u>(−2, −5), (−2, −2), (−5, −2)</u>

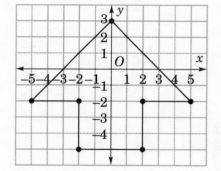

8. Plot points $B(-3, 1)$ and $C(-7, 4)$ on the coordinate plane. Draw a vertical line passing through point B and a horizontal line passing through point C. Suppose these two lines intersect at point A. What are the coordinates of point A?

   <u>(−3, 4)</u>

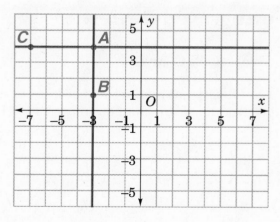

9. Describe the possible locations, in terms of quadrants or axes, for the graph of (x, y) if x and y satisfy the following conditions.

a. $xy < 0$ <u>II or IV</u>   **b.** $xy > 0$ <u>I or III</u>

10. a. Find the length of $\overline{WX}$ and the length of $\overline{XY}$.

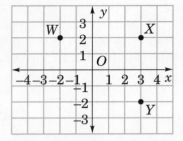

<u>$WX = 5$; $XY = 4$</u>

b. Find point Z so that figure $WXYZ$ is a rectangle.

<u>$(-2, -2)$</u>

11. A circle with center at the origin passes through the points $A(-7, 0)$, $B(7, 0)$, and $C(0, x)$ on a coordinate plane. Sketch the circle on the coordinate plane below to find the two possible values of x. <u>7, −7</u>

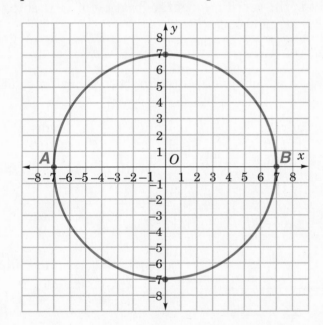

Integrated Review

Circle A, B, C, or D.

12. Which point on the number line shown below could represent the product of the numbers represented by U and V?

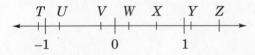

A. point T **B.** point W **C.** point Y **D.** point X

13. Find the next number of this pattern: 1, 4, 9, 61, 52, 63, . . .

A. 74   **B.** 94   **C.** 54   **D.** 65

Lesson 3-2: Reflections and Translations

Work Together

Movements of points, lines, or figures are called **transformations**. A transformation can be a flip, a slide, or a turn. Work with a partner to explore transformations on a coordinate plane.

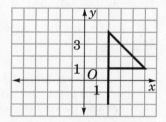

Suppose you use paint to draw the figure in the diagram. Then while the paint is still wet, fold the paper onto itself along the y-axis. An image of the figure will be transferred to the folded paper. The diagram below shows what you will see when you unfold the paper.

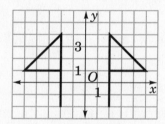

The figures in the diagram are *reflections* over the y-axis. A flip, or **reflection**, reflects an object over a line. The line is called a **line of reflection**.

1. Identify the coordinates of the vertices of the figure and its image in the diagram above.

   <u>figure: (2, 4), (5, 1), (2, 1), (2, −2); image: (−2, 4), (−5, 1), (−2, 1), (−2, −2)</u>

2. **Circle A, B, C, or D.** To reflect a point over the y-axis, multiply the x-coordinate by __?__ and use the same y-coordinate.

   A. −2   **B.** 1   **C.** −1   **D.** 0

Learn About It

When a figure is reflected over a line on a coordinate plane, every point of the original figure has a corresponding point on the other side of that line.

Example 1

Reflect the rectangle with vertices $J(-2, 1)$, $K(-2, 4)$, $M(3, 4)$, and $L(3, 1)$ over the x-axis. Identify the coordinates of the vertices of the reflected rectangle.

First plot points J, K, M, and L. Connect the points to form a rectangle.

Count how many units J is from the x-axis. Then count that many units on the opposite side of the axis. Label this point J'.

Count how many units K, L, and M are from the x-axis. Use the same method to plot K', L', and M'.

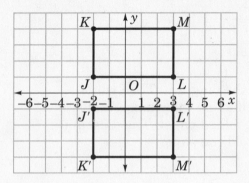

Each new point is the image of the original point. Use prime notation (M') to identify the image.

Figures and their reflected images have the same size and shape.

The coordinates of J', K', L', and M' are $J'(-2, -1)$, $K'(-2, -4)$, $L'(3, -1)$, and $M'(3, -4)$.

A slide, or **translation**, moves each point of a figure the same distance in the same direction. You can think of movements in terms of positive and negative. To the right or up is positive and to the left or down is negative.

Example 2

Points $A(-5, 2)$, $B(-3, 4)$, and $C(-1, 2)$ are the vertices of a triangle. Translate $\triangle ABC$ 6 units to the right and 3 units down. What are the coordinates of the vertices of its image?

First graph $\triangle ABC$ on a coordinate plane. Then find the points that are 6 units to the right and 3 units down from A, B, and C by adding 6 to each x-coordinate and subtracting 3 from each y-coordinate. Label the images A', B', and C'. Draw $\triangle A'B'C'$.

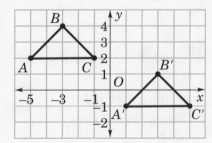

vertex		6 right, 3 down		translation
$A(-5, 2)$	+	$(6, -3)$	→	$A'(1, -1)$
$B(-3, 4)$	+	$(6, -3)$	→	$B'(3, 1)$
$C(-1, 2)$	+	$(6, -3)$	→	$C'(5, -1)$

The coordinates of A', B', and C' are $A'(1, -1)$, $B'(3, 1)$, and $C'(5, -1)$.

Apply What You've Learned

3. To reflect a point over the x-axis, use the same x-coordinate and multiply the y-coordinate by **-1** .

4. Circle A, B, C, or D. What are the coordinates of the reflection of the point $(10, 2)$ over the x-axis?

   A. $(-10, 2)$ **B.** $(-2, -10)$ **C.** $(10, -2)$ **D.** $(-2, 10)$

5. $\triangle D'E'F'$ is the reflection of $\triangle DEF$ over the y-axis. What are the coordinates of the vertices of $\triangle D'E'F'$?

   $D'(2, 4), E'(6, 3), F'(4, 1)$

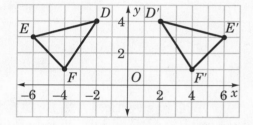

6. What are the coordinates of the image of $J(5, -3)$ after it is translated ten units up and four units to the left?

   $(1, 7)$

7. What are the coordinates of the reflection of the point $P(x, y)$ over the x-axis?

   $(x, -y)$

8. Circle A, B, C, or D. Which of the following represents the result of reflecting the figure over the y-axis and then reflecting that image over the x-axis?

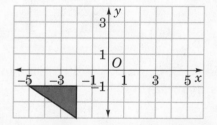

A.

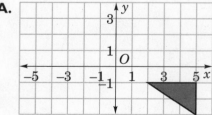

B.

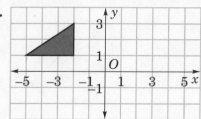

C.

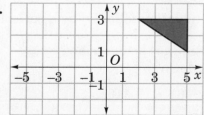

D.

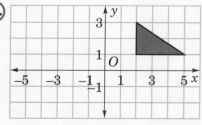

9. The graph shows a translation. Describe the translation.

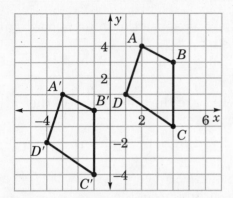

ABCD **is translated 5 units left and 3 units down.**

---

10. $\triangle ABC$ has vertices $A(2, 6)$, $B(1, 2)$, and $C(4, 5)$. Use the grid below to graph $\triangle ABC$ and its image after a translation of 6 units to the left and 4 units down.

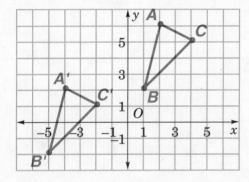

11. Circle A, B, C, or D. Which transformation was applied to $\triangle ABC$ to result in $\triangle A'B'C'$?

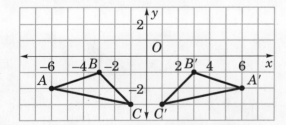

A. a reflection

C. a translation

B. a reflection followed by a translation

D. a translation followed by a reflection

12. Circle A, B, C, or D. Which of the following *cannot* be described by the translation 4 units to the left and 6 units down?

A. $A(-3, 2)$, $A'(-7, -4)$

B. $B(0, -6)$, $B'(-4, 0)$

C. $C(8, 3)$, $C'(4, -3)$

D. $D(4, -1)$, $D'(0, -7)$

13. Triangle ABC has vertex $B(4, 5)$. When $\triangle ABC$ is translated, B' has coordinates $(-2, 2)$. Describe the translation.

<u>left 6, down 3</u>

14. Circle A, B, C, or D. Suppose the figure on the grid is reflected over the line $x = 1$. Which figure shows the result?

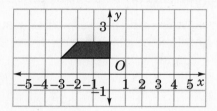

A.

B.

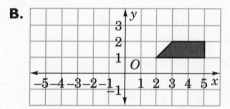

C.

D.

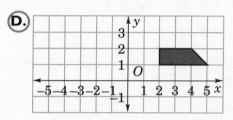

15. Latitude measures the distance above or below the equator, in degrees. The table at the right lists the latitudes of some places. If you reflected Cleveland's location over the equator, how far south would it be?

<u>40° south</u>

Place	Latitude
North Pole	90° north
Cleveland, Ohio	40° north
Equator	0°
South Pole	90° south

Integrated Review

Circle A, B, C, or D.

16. Which equation is *not* a linear relationship?

A. $y = -x$ **B.** $b = a + 6$ **C.** $x = \dfrac{1}{y}$ **D.** $2 = m - 3$

17. Suppose you want to estimate the number of bricks you could store in a shed. What must you know about the shed?

A. perimeter   **B.** area   **C.** volume   **D.** surface area

Lesson 3-3: Rotations

Learn About It

A turn about a point is called a **rotation**. The point is called the **center of rotation**. Rotations can occur in clockwise or counterclockwise directions. The amount of the rotation can be described in degrees.

When the hand of a clock moves, it is said to rotate clockwise about the center of the clock. When the hand of the clock moves from 12 to 3, the hand has rotated through a 90° angle.

1. Suppose the hand of the clock is at 12 o'clock. What is the new position of the hand if it is rotated through a 180° angle?

<u>6 o'clock</u>

2. Explain why it is *not* necessary to indicate if a 180° rotation is clockwise or counterclockwise.

<u>Answers may vary. Sample: clockwise and counterclockwise</u>

<u>rotations of 180° about the same point produce the same image.</u>

You can use a center of rotation that lies inside a figure.

Example 1

Draw the image of rectangle *ABCD* after a rotation of 90° counterclockwise about the origin.

First draw $\overline{OB}$. Moving counterclockwise, draw a ray that makes a 90° angle with $\overline{OB}$. Mark *B'* so that *OB = OB'*. *B'* is the image of *B*.

Repeat this process for the other three vertices. Connect the images to complete the rotation.

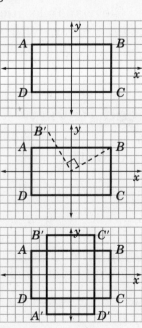

You can use a point on a figure as the center of rotation.

Example 2

$\triangle DEF$ has vertices $D(0, 0)$, $E(0, 4)$, and $F(3, 0)$. Draw the image of $\triangle DEF$ after a rotation of 90° clockwise about the origin.

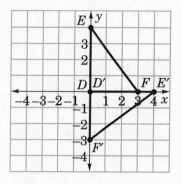

First rotate each vertex 90° clockwise to produce its image. Then connect the images to complete the rotation.

$\triangle D'E'F'$ has vertices $D'(0, 0)$, $E'(4, 0)$, and $F'(0, -3)$.

Apply What You've Learned
Estimates may vary. Samples given.

3. **Estimation** Rotations other than 90°, 180°, and 270° are also possible. Each figure below is an image formed by rotating clockwise the figure at the right. Estimate each rotation.

a.

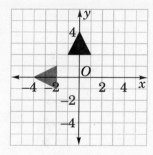

<u>45° clockwise</u>

b.

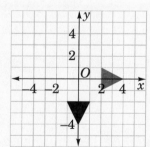

<u>225° clockwise</u>

For each of the following, draw the image of the figure under the given rotation about the origin.

4. 90° counterclockwise

5. 270° clockwise

6. Describe a pattern for finding the coordinates of a point (a, b) after a 180° counterclockwise rotation about the origin.

<u>$(-a, -b)$</u>

7. Circle A, B, C, or D. Which of the following gives the coordinates of a point (a, b) after a 270° clockwise rotation about the origin?

A. $(-a, b)$ **B.** $(-a, -b)$ **C.** $(b, -a)$ **(D.)** $(-b, a)$

8. Explain why $\triangle ABC$ is an image of $\triangle DEF$ after either a rotation or a reflection.

<u>Answers may vary. Sample: a 180°</u>

<u>rotation about the origin and a</u>

<u>reflection over the y-axis give the</u>

<u>same image of $\triangle ABC$, which is $\triangle DEF$.</u>

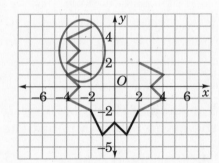

9. You and your date are having a dinner at a revolving restaurant at the top of the Needle in Seattle.

a. Suppose that you are facing north when seated and that by the time you take the last bite of dessert you have rotated 270° clockwise. In what direction are you facing?

<u>west</u>

b. If you had eaten more slowly, you may have rotated 540°. What direction would you be facing in this situation?

<u>south</u>

10. Rotate the figure at the right 90° counterclockwise about the origin. Then reflect the result over the y-axis. Finally, translate the result 3 units up. Show each figure as created and circle your final image.

Integrated Review

Circle A, B, C, or D.

11. $\overline{DF}$ is x units long, and $\overline{EF}$ is y units long. What is the length of $\overline{DE}$?

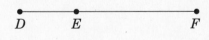

A. $x + y$ **(B.)** $x - y$ **C.** $y - x$ **D.** xy

12. If $x = 4$, which of the following does *not* equal 16?

A. x^2 **B.** $(-x)^2$ **C.** $(-x)(-x)$ **(D.)** $-x^2$

Lesson 3-4: Manipulating Shapes

Work Together

Look at the right triangle shown below. The lengths of the sides of the triangle are 6 units, 8 units, and 10 units. Trace this triangle and then cut it out. Make two copies of the triangle. Label the sides of the triangles as shown below. Work with a partner to make four-sided figures by matching congruent sides. Sketch each of these figures. Then find the perimeter and area of each of these figures.

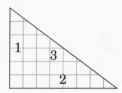

If you match the sides labeled "1", the figure formed is a parallelogram. Its perimeter is 36 units and its area is 48 sq. units.

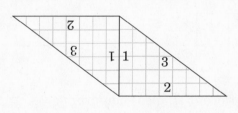

$P = 2(l + w)$

$\quad = 2(10 + 8)$

$\quad = 36 \text{ units}$

$A = b \times h$

$\quad = 6 \times 8$

$\quad = 48 \text{ sq. units}$

1. On the grid at the right, sketch the figure formed when you match the sides labeled "2." Identify the type of quadrilateral formed. Find the area and perimeter of this quadrilateral.

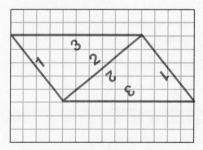

The figure is a __parallelogram__.

Perimeter = __32 units__

Area = __48 sq. units__

2. On the grid at the right, sketch the figure formed when you match the sides labeled "3." Identify the type of quadrilateral formed. Find the area and perimeter of this quadrilateral.

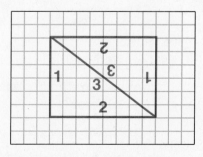

The figure is a __rectangle__.

Perimeter = __28 units__

Area = __48 sq. units__

3. What do you notice about the areas of the figures formed? Support your answer with an explanation.

<u>Answers may vary. Sample: all the figures have the same area. Each</u>

<u>figure has area equal to the sum of the areas of the triangles.</u>

Apply What You've Learned

4. Each of the small boxes in the figures is a square. All the squares are the same size. If the perimeter of the figure at the right is 24, find the perimeter and area of each figure shown below.

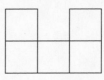

a. $P = \underline{24}$ $A = \underline{20}$ **b.** $P = \underline{24}$ $A = \underline{20}$ **c.** $P = \underline{20}$ $A = \underline{20}$

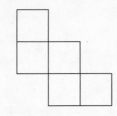
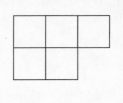

d. How do the perimeters of the different shapes compare?

<u>Answers may vary. Sample: the perimeters are different.</u>

e. How do the areas of the different shapes compare?

<u>The areas are all the same.</u>

f. Which of these figures could you fold to form a box without a top?

<u>a, b</u>

5. Circle A, B, C, or D.   Which figure *cannot* be formed by matching a pair of corresponding sides of two congruent isosceles triangles?

A. triangle   **B.** rectangle

C. trapezoid   **D.** parallelogram

6. Suppose you are using square tiles to make a rectangle. You have 12 tiles and each tile measures 1 in. on a side.

a. What are the dimensions of a rectangle with the greatest possible perimeter?

<u>1 in. by 12 in.</u>

b. What are the dimensions of a rectangle with the least possible perimeter?

<u>3 in. by 4 in.</u>

7. Suppose you put two congruent copies of this trapezoid together to form a parallelogram.

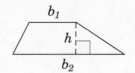

a. What will be the length of the base of the parallelogram?

$b_1 + b_2$

b. What will be the height of the parallelogram?

h

c. What is an expression for the area of the parallelogram?

$h(b_1 + b_2)$

d. What is an expression for the area of the trapezoid?

$\frac{1}{2}h(b_1 + b_2)$

8. On the grid below, draw four congruent equilateral triangles so that they form: **Answers may vary. Samples given.**

a. a parallelogram

b. a triangle

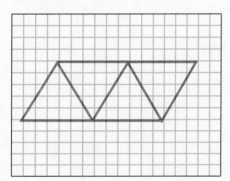

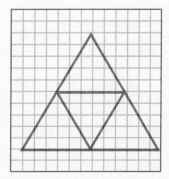

Integrated Review

Circle A, B, C, or D.

9. The vertices of $\triangle ABC$ are $A(-4, 2)$, $B(-3, 4)$, and $C(-2, 2)$. This triangle is translated. The new coordinates for point A are $(2, 2)$ and for point B are $(3, 4)$. What are the new coordinates for point C?

A. $(2, 8)$ **B.** $(4, 2)$ **C.** $(-2, 8)$ **D.** $(-8, 2)$

10. What happens to the area of a figure after a reflection?

A. The area increases.   **B.** The area decreases.

C. The area remains the same.   **D.** The area doubles.

Lesson 3-5: The Pythagorean Theorem

Work Together

The two shorter sides of a right triangle are the **legs** of the right triangle. The side opposite the right angle is the **hypotenuse**. The hypotenuse is always the longest side.

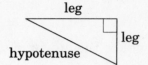

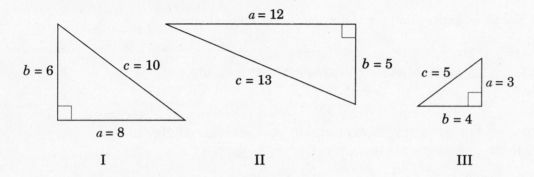

I   II   III

1. Using the three right triangles shown above, work with your partner to complete the following table.

	a	b	c	a^2	b^2	c^2
I	8	6	10	64	36	100
II	12	5	13	144	25	169
III	3	4	5	9	16	25

2. Look for a pattern. What is true about the squares of the lengths of the sides of a right triangle?

<u>The square of the length of the hypotenuse is equal to the sum of the</u>

<u>squares of the lengths of the legs.</u>

_____

Learn About It

In any right triangle the square of the length c of the hypotenuse is equal to the sum of the squares of the lengths a and b of the legs.

$$c^2 = a^2 + b^2$$

This property is called the **Pythagorean theorem**.

Example 1

The baselines of a baseball diamond form a square with side lengths of 90 ft. When a runner on first base tries to steal second base, the catcher has to throw from home to second. How far is that throw?

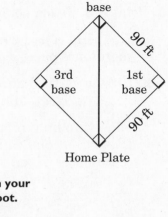

$$c^2 = a^2 + b^2$$ **Use the Pythagorean theorem.**

$$c^2 = 90^2 + 90^2$$ **Substitute 90 for a and 90 for b.**

$$c^2 = 8100 + 8100$$

$$c^2 = 16,200$$ **Add.**

$$c = \sqrt{16,200}$$ **You can use the square root key $\boxed{\sqrt{x}}$ on your calculator to find the positive square root.**

$$c \approx 127.3$$ **Round your answer to the nearest tenth.**

The catcher has to throw the ball 127.3 ft.

If you know the lengths of two sides of a right triangle, you can use the Pythagorean theorem to find the length of the third side.

Example 2

The size of a television screen is given by the length of its diagonal. Sandro is buying a television with a 20-in. screen. An advertisement describes the screen as being 12 in. tall but does not mention the width. Find the width of the television screen.

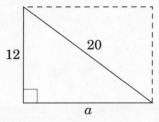

The 20-in. diagonal is the hypotenuse of a right triangle with a leg that measures 12 in. The length of the other leg is the width of the screen.

$$c^2 = a^2 + b^2$$ **Use the Pythagorean theorem.**

$$20^2 = a^2 + 12^2$$ **Substitute 20 for c and 12 for b.**

$$400 = a^2 + 144$$

$$400 - 144 = a^2 + 144 - 144$$ **Subtract 144 from both sides.**

$$256 = a^2$$

$$\sqrt{256} = a$$ **Find the positive square root.**

$$16 = a$$

The width of the television screen is 16 in.

When two points do not lie on a horizontal or vertical line, you can find the distance between the points by using the Pythagorean theorem.

3. Point $A(3, 2)$ and point $B(-3, -2)$ are the endpoints of a segment.

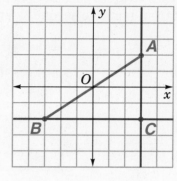

a. Plot point A and point B on the coordinate plane shown.

b. Draw a vertical line through point A and a horizontal line through point B.

c. These two lines intersect at a point. Label this point C. What are the coordinates of point C?

<u>(3, −2)</u>

d. Find the length of $\overline{AC}$ and the length of $\overline{BC}$.

<u>$AC = 4$, $BC = 6$</u>

e. Notice that $\triangle ABC$ is a right triangle. Use the Pythagorean theorem to find the length of $\overline{AB}$.

<u>$AB = \sqrt{52} \approx 7.2$</u>

Apply What You've Learned

4. Circle A, B, C, or D. Which statement is true for this triangle?

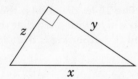

A. $x^2 = z^2 + y^2$　　　　　　　**B.** $y^2 = x^2 + z^2$

C. $y^2 = z^2 - x^2$　　　　　　　**D.** $z^2 = x^2 + y^2$

5. Find the missing length in each right triangle.

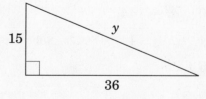

a.

<u>20</u>

b.

<u>39</u>

6. Circle A, B, C, or D. What is the perimeter of a right triangle with legs measuring 9 ft and 12 ft?

(A.) 36 ft   **B.** 42 ft   **C.** 15 ft   **D.** 25 ft

7. Suppose you know that the length of $\overline{AB}$ is 7 m and the length of $\overline{BC}$ is 24 m.

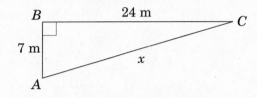

   a. What is the length of $\overline{AC}$?

   <u>25 m</u>

   b. What is the perimeter of $\triangle ABC$?

   <u>56 m</u>

   c. What is the area of $\triangle ABC$?

   <u>84 m²</u>

8. Use the map to answer the following questions.

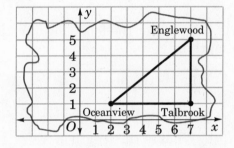

   a. What is the distance from Oceanview to Talbrook?

   <u>5</u>

   b. What is the distance from Talbrook to Englewood?

   <u>4</u>

   c. What is the distance from Englewood to Oceanview?

   <u>$\sqrt{41} \approx 6.4$</u>

   d. If each unit on the grid represents 4 miles, what is the actual distance from Englewood to Oceanview? Round your answer to the nearest mile.

   <u>26 mi</u>

Integrated Review

Circle A, B, C, or D.

9. If $3x - 2 = 6 + 8x$, then $x = $ __?__ .

   A. $\frac{4}{5}$ **(B.)** $\frac{-8}{5}$ **C.** $\frac{8}{5}$ **D.** $\frac{-4}{5}$

10. Which of the numbers below is *not* equal to the other three?

   A. 130%   **B.** $\frac{13}{10}$ **(C.)** 1.3×10^2 **D.** $\sqrt{1.69}$

Lesson 3-6: Using a Diagram

Learn About It

You can use the diagram below to solve the following problem.

> *ABCD* is a square with sides of length 4. The midpoints of the sides are *E*, *F*, *G*, and *H*. What is the area of *EFGH*?

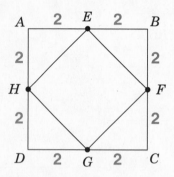

As you answer the following questions, add the new information to the diagram.

1. What is the area of *ABCD*? <u>16</u>

2. a. What is the length of $\overline{AE}$? <u>2</u>

    b. What is the length of $\overline{AH}$? <u>2</u>

    c. Calculate the area of △*AHE*. <u>2</u>

3. Determine the lengths of the legs of the other triangles.
<u>*EB* = 2, *BF* = 2, *CF* = 2, *CG* = 2, *DG* = 2, *DH* = 2</u>

4. What do you know about the areas of the four triangles?
<u>They are equal.</u>

5. Looking at the diagram above, explain how you can find the area of *EFGH* using your answers from Questions 1-4.
<u>Answers may vary. Sample: subtract the area of the triangles from the area of *ABCD*.</u>

6. What is the area of *EFGH*?
<u>8</u>

7. Describe another way to find the area of *EFGH*.
<u>Answers may vary. Sample: calculate *EF*, *FG*, *GH*, and *HE* by the Pythagorean theorem, then calculate the area of *EFGH*.</u>

A diagram can help you to see a problem and its solution more clearly. Work with a partner to solve the following problem.

8. A lawn sprinkler rotates and waters a circular pattern that has a radius of 15 ft. It is set in the middle of a square lawn that measures 30 ft wide and 30 ft long.

a. What is the area of the entire lawn?

900 ft^2

b. What is the area of the circular region being watered?

706.9 ft^2

c. Explain how to find the area of the region *not* being watered.

__Subtract the area of the circle from the area of the square.__

d. What is the area of the region *not* being watered?

193.1 ft^2

Apply What You've Learned

9. A treasure hunter follows these directions:

Start at the front of the cave and walk 40 ft north. Turn and walk 30 ft west. Dig here.

The treasure hunter's parrot flew directly from the front door to the location where the treasure hunter was digging. How far is this distance?

50 ft

10. Circle A, B, C, or D. If $\triangle ABC \cong \triangle DEF$, $AB = 27$ ft, $m\angle B = 39°$, and $m\angle F = 57°$, which of the following statements is false?

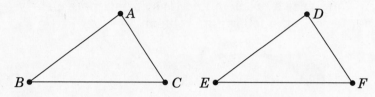

A. $AC = DF$

B. $\overline{AB} \cong \overline{DE}$

C. $m\angle E = 84°$

D. $\angle C \cong \angle F$

11. The coordinates of the endpoints of a segment are $C(2, 6)$ and $D(-4, 1)$.

a. Plot the points on the grid below.

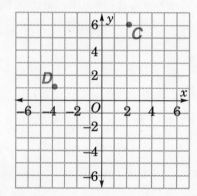

b. Find the length of $\overline{CD}$.

$\sqrt{61} \approx 7.8$

12. The baselines of a softball diamond form a square with a side length of 60 feet. The right fielder catches a ball on the first baseline, 20 feet beyond first base. How far does she have to throw the ball to reach third base?

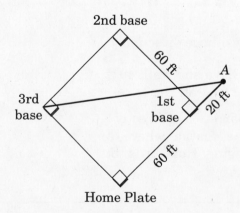

100 ft

13. Suppose you have three sticks and the lengths of the three sticks are 6 cm, 9 cm, and 11 cm. Explain how you can use these sticks to measure a length of 14 cm.

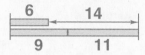

14. a. Plot the following points on the grid below: $A(-5, -2)$, $B(5, -2)$ and $C(5, 8)$.

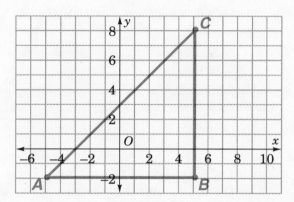

b. Points A, B, and C are the vertices of a triangle. Sketch the triangle.

c. Circle A, B, C, or D. Which of the following choices can be used in the blank below to give a correct statement?

Triangle ABC is _____ triangle.

A. an obtuse **B.** an equilateral

C. a scalene **D.** an isosceles

Integrated Review

Circle A, B, C, or D.

15. How many different ways can you combine coins to total $.29?

A. 13 **B.** 10 **C.** 9 **D.** 12

16. In which set are all three values equal?

A. 52%, 0.052, $\frac{52}{100}$ **B.** 0.52%, 0.52, $\frac{52}{100}$

C. 52%, 0.52, $\frac{52}{100}$ **D.** 0.52%, 0.0052, $\frac{52}{100}$

Lesson 3-7: Fractals

Learn About It

Self-similar shapes or objects can be created by repeated additions to a figure or by repeated subtractions from a figure. A figure is **self-similar** if each part of the figure is similar to the whole figure. A figure with this property is a **fractal**.

The first three stages of a pattern called the *Sierpinski triangle* are shown below.

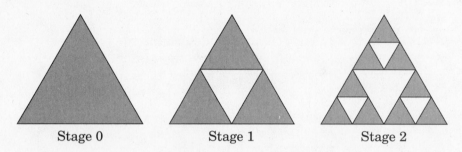

Stage 0   Stage 1   Stage 2

The triangles above are self-similar. The pattern is generated by repeatedly locating the midpoint of each side of the triangle, connecting the midpoints to form four new triangles, and then dropping the middle triangle. Stages 3 and 4 of the Sierpinski triangle are shown below.

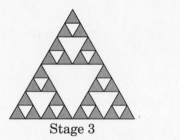 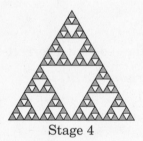

Stage 3   Stage 4

1. Complete this table for the Sierpinski triangle.

Stage	0	1	2	3	4
Number of shaded triangles	1	3	9	27	81

2. What pattern(s) do you see in the table?

   <u>At each stage, the number of shaded triangles triples.</u>

3. Let n represent the number of the stage. Write an expression for the number of shaded triangles at Stage n.

   3^n

Self-similar shapes or objects can be created by hand or by using a computer. Let's investigate other interesting fractals.

Example 1

The first three stages of a pattern, called *Cantor Dust*, are shown below. How many segments will there be in Stage 3 and in Stage 4?

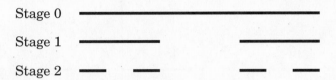

Stage 0

Stage 1

Stage 2

In order to answer this question, you need to determine the pattern. At each stage, you see that the middle third of each segment in the preceding stage has been removed. This means that in Stage 3 there will be 8 segments and in Stage 4 there will be 16 segments.

4. Draw Stage 3 and Stage 4 of the fractal Cantor Dust.

Stage 3 ‒ ‒   ‒ ‒   ‒ ‒   ‒ ‒

Stage 4 ·· ··   ·· ··   ·· ··   ·· ··

5. Complete the table below for the fractal Cantor Dust.

Stage	0	1	2	3	4
Number of segments	1	2	4	8	16

6. What pattern(s) do you see in the table?

   At each stage, the number of segments doubles.

7. How many segments will there be in Stage 9?

   512 segments

8. Let n represent the number of the stage. Write an expression for the number of segments at Stage n.

   2^n

Apply What You've Learned

9. **Circle A, B, C, or D.** How many shaded triangles will there be at Stage 10 of the Sierpinski triangle?

   A. 30 **(B.)** 59,049 **C.** 24 **D.** 19,683

10. The figures below show the first two stages of a fractal. This fractal is generated by repeating the following steps.

Stage 0: Draw a single stem that ends with a point.

Stage 1: Add 4 branches to the stem. Add an endpoint to each one of the stems.

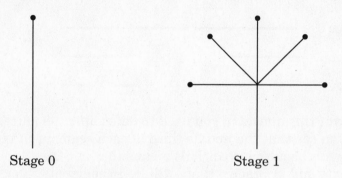

Stage 0   Stage 1

a. How many endpoints are there in Stage 1?

5 endpoints _____

b. Draw Stage 2 of the fractal.

c. How many endpoints are there in Stage 2?

25 endpoints _____

d. Complete the table below for the fractal.

Stage	0	1	2	3	4
Number of points	1	5	25	125	625

e. Circle A, B, C, or D. Let n represent the number of the stage. Which of the following is an expression for the number of endpoints at Stage n?

A. $5n$ **B.** n^5 **C.** 5^n **D.** $n + 5$

11. The first three stages of a fractal pattern are shown below. Describe the steps that you use to obtain each stage.

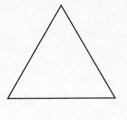
Stage 0

Stage 1

Stage 2

<u>Answers may vary. Sample: construct an equilateral triangle. On the</u>
<u>middle third of each side, construct another equilateral triangle, then</u>
<u>remove the base of the smaller triangle.</u>

12. The first two stages of a fractal pattern are shown below. Draw Stage 2 of the fractal.

Stage 0

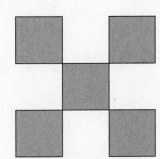
Stage 1

Stage 2

Integrated Review

Circle A, B, C, or D.

13. What is the perimeter of a right triangle with legs measuring 8 cm and 15 cm?

   A. 40 cm   **B.** 60 cm

   C. 46 cm   **D.** 120 cm

14. The scale on a map is $\frac{1}{4}$ in. = 17 mi. Two cities are shown as being 5 in. apart on the map. What is the actual distance in miles?

   A. 3.4 mi   **B.** 68 mi

   C. 85 mi   **D.** 340 mi

Lesson 3-8: Three-Dimensional Figures

Learn About It

Figures that do not lie in a plane are *space figures*, or *three-dimensional figures*. Some space figures are shown below.

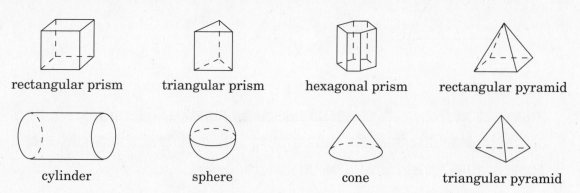

rectangular prism triangular prism hexagonal prism rectangular pyramid

cylinder sphere cone triangular pyramid

Prisms are three-dimensional figures with two parallel and congruent polygonal faces, called *bases*. A **pyramid** is a three-dimensional figure with only one base. Both prisms and pyramids are named by the shapes of their bases.

Work Together

Work with a partner to explore the characteristics of three-dimensional figures. Consider the figure shown below. It is made up of unit cubes.

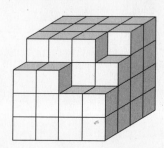

1. a. How many unit cubes make up the bottom layer of this figure?

   <u>16 unit cubes</u>

b. How many unit cubes make up the entire figure as shown?

   <u>57 unit cubes</u>

c. If you want to add unit cubes to make the object a large solid cube, how many unit cubes would you need to add?

   <u>7 unit cubes</u>

When manufacturers make boxes for products, the patterns are cut from cardboard and then folded into boxes. The cost of the package is part of the price of the product. Manufacturers consider the *surface area* of a package when they calculate the price. The **surface area** of a prism is the sum of the areas of the faces.

Example 1

Find the surface area of the figure.

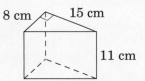

To find the surface area, you need to know the dimensions of each face of the prism. This prism is made up of two congruent right triangles and three rectangles. Each triangle has a base length of 15 cm and a height of 8 cm.

To find the dimensions of the rectangles, you need to know the length of the hypotenuse of the right triangle. Use the Pythagorean theorem.

$$8^2 + 15^2 = c^2$$

$$289 = c^2$$

$$17 = c$$

The hypotenuse is 17 cm.

The dimensions of the three rectangles are 17 cm by 11 cm, 8 cm by 11 cm, and 15 cm by 11 cm.

Next, recall the area formulas.

$$\text{rectangle: } A = lw \qquad \text{triangle: } A = \tfrac{1}{2}bh$$

$$\text{Surface Area} = (17 \times 11) + (8 \times 11) + (15 \times 11) + (2)\left(\tfrac{1}{2} \times 8 \times 15\right)$$

$$= 187 + 88 + 165 + 120$$

$$= 560 \text{ cm}^2$$

The surface area of the figure is 560 cm^2.

Apply What You've Learned

2. **Circle A, B, C, or D.** The surface area of this figure is 52,800 in.^{2}. What is the value of x?

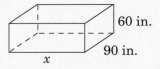

A. 120 in.   **B.** 130 in.

C. 140 in.   **D.** 150 in.

3. Look at the object below. Unit cubes have been removed from the middle to create a tunnel that goes through the entire object.

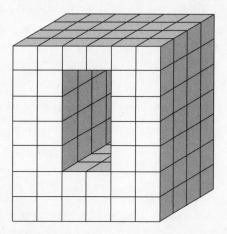

a. How many unit cubes make up this object?

136 unit cubes

b. If this had been a solid block to start, how many unit cubes were removed?

32 unit cubes

4. A rectangular prism is formed using exactly 30 cubes. How many different prisms can be formed? Explain.

5 prisms; they have dimensions 1 × 1 × 30, 1 × 2 × 15, 1 × 3 × 10, 1 × 5 × 6, and 2 × 3 × 5.

5. If a coin were placed on its edge and spun, its path would describe a three-dimensional figure. What would that figure be?

a sphere

6. Circle A, B, C, or D. △ABC is rotated 360° about side $\overline{AB}$. Which of the following three-dimensional solids is formed?

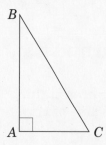

A. pyramid   **B.** sphere   **C.** cylinder   **D.** cone

7. Draw a diagram and find the surface area of a triangular prism with a height of 12 cm whose base is a right triangle with legs of 7 cm and 24 cm.

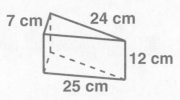

7 cm 24 cm 12 cm 25 cm

$$\text{surface area} = (7 \times 12) + (24 \times 12) + (25 \times 12) + 2\left(\tfrac{1}{2}\right)(7)(24) = 840 \text{ cm}^2$$

8. Circle A, B, C, or D. Find which pattern(s) *cannot* be folded to make a closed box.

(A.)

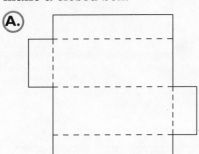

B.

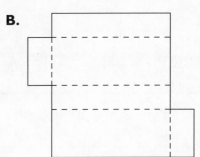

C.

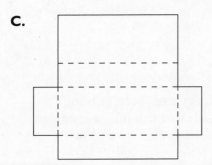

D.

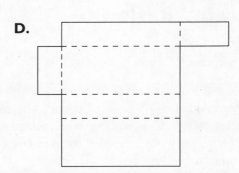

9. Unit cubes are stacked to form the object shown below. How many additional cubes must be added to the stacked cubes to form an object that has dimensions of 3 units by 3 units by 3 units?

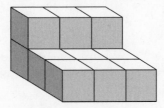

15 cubes

10. The figure shown can be cut out and folded on the lines to form a three-dimensional box.

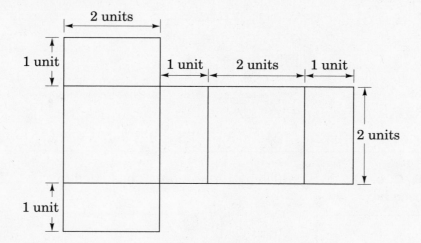

a. Determine the surface area of the box.

16 sq. units

b. Determine the volume of the box.

4 cu. units

Integrated Review

Circle A, B, C, or D.

11. Claire got an answer of 4.89 when she entered 24 on her calculator and pressed the $\sqrt{x}$ key. As usual, she stopped to think briefly about whether or not this answer was reasonable. Which of the following is the most likely explanation for her to believe that the answer is or is not reasonable?

A. It is not reasonable because the answer should be a whole number.

B. It is reasonable because 4 squared is 16 while 5 squared is 25.

C. It is not reasonable because the answer should be only slightly more than 4.

D. It is reasonable because 24 is an even number.

12. One leg of a right triangle is twice as long as the other leg. If the length of the shorter leg is x, which of the expressions below represents the area of that triangle?

A. x^2 **B.** $2x^2$ **C.** $2x$ **D.** $\frac{1}{2}x$

Lesson 3-9: Answering Open-Ended Questions

Work Together

You can work with a partner to improve your skills at answering open-ended questions. First work individually to answer the following question.

1. The large block shown is made up of 64 unit cubes. Suppose the outside of the large block is painted. Categorize the 64 unit cubes by the number of sides that are painted. Present a detailed explanation to support your answer.   **Answers may vary. Check students' work.**

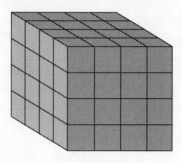

2. The scoring guide explains exactly how answers are scored. Exchange work with your partner and use the scoring guide to score each other's answer.

   Score: **Answers may vary. Check students' work.**

   _____

Scoring Guide

3   You recognize that each cube may have either 0, 1, 2, or 3 sides painted and you correctly calculate the number of each kind of cube. (0 sides = 8; 1 side = 24; 2 sides = 24; 3 sides = 8)

2   You recognize that each cube may have either 0, 1, 2, or 3 sides painted but you make a computational error.

or

You recognize that each cube may have either 0, 1, 2, or 3 sides painted but for certain cubes you identify incorrectly the number of sides painted.

or

You do not consider all four of the categories for the number of painted sides but you correctly calculate the number of sides painted for the ones that you list.

1   You do not consider all the categories for the number of painted sides and you make a computational error.

or

You give an answer with no explanation.

0   You answer the question inappropriately

or

You fail to attempt an answer.

Learn About It

Here are three sample responses.
Answers may vary. Samples given.
Sample 1

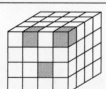

corners: $4 \times 2 = 8$
edges: $8 \times 6 = 48$
middle: $4 \times 6 = 24$
inside: $4 \times 2 = 8$

The cubes can have either 3, 2, 1, or 0 sides painted. The corner cubes have 3 sides painted, the cubes on the edges have 2 sides painted, the middle cubes have 1 side painted, and the inside cubes have 0 sides painted. There are 8 corner cubes, 48 cubes on the edges, 24 cubes in the middle, and 8 cubes on the inside.

So 8 cubes have 3 sides painted, 48 cubes have 2 sides painted, 24 cubes have 1 side painted, and 8 cubes have 0 sides painted.

3. This response scored a **2**. Explain why. <u>It is correct except for a</u>
<u>computational error with the number of edge cubes.</u>

Sample 2

total cubes $\underset{\underline{8}}{64}$ (3 sides painted)

$\overline{56}$ (2 sides painted)

$\underset{\overline{32}}{-24}$ 1 side painted

The cubes can have either 3, 2, or 1 sides painted. There are 8 cubes with 3 sides painted, 24 cubes with 2 sides painted, and 32 cubes with 1 side painted.

4. This response scored a **1**. Explain why. <u>The response missed the</u>
<u>unpainted cubes and made a computational error.</u>

Sample 3

All of the sides of the block are painted.

5. This response scored a **0**. Explain why. <u>The question is answered</u>
<u>inappropriately.</u>

6. Look back at your answer to Question 1. If you did not score a **3**, use
what you have learned to write an improved answer.
Answers may vary. Check students' work.

7. The vertices of $\triangle ABC$ are $A(0, 0)$, $B(-5, 0)$, and $C(0, 5)$. Reflect $\triangle ABC$ over the y-axis. Then reflect the image over the x-axis. Then reflect the second image over the y-axis. Describe the figure formed by $\triangle ABC$ and its images.

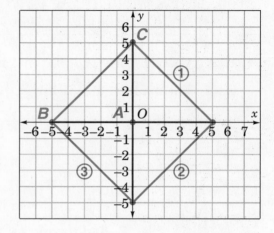

3   Correct sketch ($\triangle ABC$ in quadrant II, first image in quadrant I, second image in quadrant IV, and third image in quadrant III) **AND** identification that figure is a square.

2   Incorrect reflection (over wrong axis) with correct identification of figure **OR** incorrect quadrilateral to describe final figure.

1   Incorrect translation of original triangle (rotation or translation).

0   Inappropriate response or no response.

8. A major league baseball diamond is a square that is 90 ft on each side. Suppose the shortstop is standing right on the line between second and third base. Describe how the Pythagorean theorem could be used to find the distance from the shortstop to home plate.

3   Correct description of how to find the shorter leg of the triangle (measure from third base or measure from second base and subtract from 90) **AND** correct description of use of Pythagorean theorem to find the distance from the shortstop to home plate.

2   Finds the shorter and longer legs **AND** states the Pythagorean theorem, but applies it incorrectly.

1   Finds the length of the shorter leg **OR** states the Pythagorean theorem incorrectly.

0   Inappropriate response or no response.

Chapter Review

Circle A, B, C, or D.

1. The coordinates of point B are $(-7, 2)$ and the coordinates of point C are $(8, 10)$. Find the length of $\overline{BC}$.

   A. 8 units   **(B.)** 17 units   **C.** 15 units   **D.** 23 units

2. Performing which set of transformations on the white figure below will *not* result in the white figure covering the black figure entirely?

   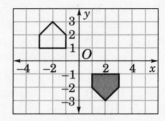

   A. reflection over the y-axis followed by reflection over the x-axis

   B. translation 4 units to the right followed by reflection over the x-axis

   (C.) reflection over the y-axis followed by translation 4 units down

   D. rotation of 180° about the origin

3. If the figure at the right were translated 3 units to the left and then reflected over the x-axis, which figure below would show the result?

   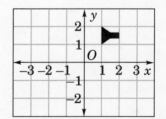

   A.

   B.

   (C.)

   D.

   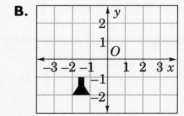

   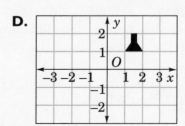

4. A figure is made of layers of unit cubes stacked one above the other. A $2 \times 3 \times 4$ block of unit cubes has been removed. Assume that no other cubes have been removed. How many unit cubes are contained in the structure shown?

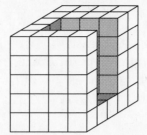

A. 76   **B.** 82

C. 94   **D.** 100

5. From the four types of boxes shown, you must choose a type of box to hold exactly one dozen blocks of cheese. Each of the cheese blocks is a *rectangular parallelepiped* (a solid with six faces, each of which is a parallelogram). The dimensions for each cheese block are 1 in. by 2 in. by 6 in. The measurements shown for each type of box are its interior dimensions. Which type of box must you choose to minimize the amount of unfilled space left inside the box after it has been packed with cheese blocks?

A.
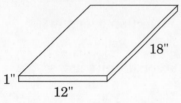

B.
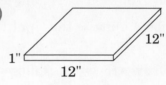

C.
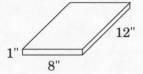

D.
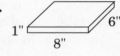

6. Suppose you know that the length of line segment AB is 15 cm and the length of line segment AC is 25 cm. Find the perimeter of $\triangle ABC$.

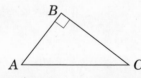

A. 300 cm   **B.** 150 cm   **C.** 400 cm   **D.** 60 cm

7. The vertices of rectangle $ABCD$ are $A(-3, -1)$, $B(-1, -1)$, $C(-1, -4)$, and $D(-3, -4)$. Which of the following gives the coordinates of the image after a rotation of 180° clockwise about the origin?

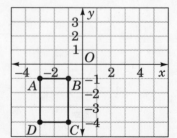

A. $A'(-3, 1)$, $B'(-1, 1)$, $C'(-1, 4)$, $D'(-3, 4)$

B. $A'(3, 1)$, $B'(1, 1)$, $C'(1, 4)$, $D'(3, 4)$

C. $A'(-3, -1)$, $B'(-1, -1)$, $C'(-1, -4)$, $D'(-3, -4)$

D. $A'(3, -1)$, $B'(1, -1)$, $C'(1, -4)$, $D'(3, -4)$

Write your answer in the boxes at the top of the grid, one number (or decimal point) per box. Then fill in the corresponding circle below each box.

8. The first three stages of a pattern are shown below. How many branches will there be in Stage 6?

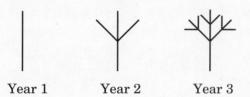

Year 1   Year 2   Year 3

2	4	3	
/	/	/	/
.	.	.	.
0	0	0	0
1	1	1	1
2	2	2	2
3	3	**3**	3
4	**4**	4	4
5	5	5	5
6	6	6	6
7	7	7	7
8	8	8	8
9	9	9	9

Answer the following open-ended question in the space below.

9. The vertices of $\triangle ABC$ are $A(1, 3)$, $B(3, 1)$, and $C(3, 3)$. Find the coordinates of the vertices of its image after a rotation of 90° clockwise about the origin. Sketch $\triangle ABC$ and its image $\triangle A'B'C'$. What is the area of $\triangle A'B'C'$? How does it compare with the area of $\triangle ABC$? Show your work and explain how you found your answer.

3   Correct coordinates of $\triangle A'B'C'$ (A' (3, –1), B' (1, –3), C' (3, –3)) **AND** correct graph of $\triangle ABC$ and $\triangle A'B'C'$ **AND** correct area of each triangle (2 sq. units) **AND** explanation that area stays the same during a rotation.

2   Incorrect translation (rotation the wrong way or translation or reflection) with graph reflecting the wrong translation **OR** different areas for the two triangles.

1   One part missing (area, sketches, or coordinates), **OR** two parts wrong.

0   Inappropriate response or no response.

Alternative Assessment Projects

Here are some projects that will demonstrate your understanding of the topics in this chapter.

Project 1

Create two examples each of a reflection, a translation, and a rotation. Include an explanation of how you made each transformation.

3 The student creates two examples of a reflection, a translation, and a rotation, and explains all of them.

2 The student creates one example of a reflection, a translation, and a rotation, and explains all of them.

1 The student creates at least one example of a reflection, a translation, or a rotation.

0 The student answers inappropriately or fails to attempt an answer.

Project 2

Go to the library and research fractals. Prepare a presentation that includes pictures of different stages of some interesting fractals and an explanation of how fractals are created.

3 The student investigates fractals in the library, and prepares a presentation that includes pictures and a clear explanation of how they are generated.

2 The student investigates fractals in the library, and prepares a presentation that includes pictures, but no clear explanation.

1 The student investigates fractals in the library, but does not prepare a presentation.

0 The student answers inappropriately or fails to attempt an answer.

Lesson 4-1: Range, Mean, Mode, and Median

Learn About It

The **range** of a set of data is the difference between the greatest and least values. The **mean**, which is also called the average, is found by adding all of the values and dividing by the number of values. The **mode** is the value that occurs most frequently. The **median** is the middle value when the values are arranged in numerical order. When there is an even number of values, a set of data will have two middle values. In this case, to find the median, add the middle values and divide by two.

Consider the following hourly wages, in dollars, of the night shift at Burger Land.

5.00   4.50   4.50   4.50   5.25   6.00   5.00

6.00   4.50   4.50   6.00   14.00   5.00

1. Arrange the wages in order from least to greatest. 4.50   4.50   4.50   4.50

4.50   5.00   5.00   5.00   5.25   6.00   6.00   6.00   14.00

2. Find the range by subtracting the least value from the greatest value.

9.50

3. There are 13 data items. When the data items are listed in order, the median is the middle, or seventh value. Find the median.

5.00

4. Find the mode, by finding the value that occurs most frequently. 4.50

5. Calculate the mean by finding the sum of all of the values and dividing by 13.

5.75

If a value is much higher or lower than most of the data, it is called an **outlier**. In the Burger Land data, the $14.00 wage is an outlier. An outlier can affect the sum of data so that the mean does not represent the data well. The median is not affected by an outlier, because the median is the middle value.

6. a. In the Burger Land data, the $14.00 wage is the manager's wage. Leave out this wage and find the new mean, median, and mode.

mean 5.06   median 5.00   mode 4.50

b. Which value in part (a) changed the most from its original value?

mean

Use the following math exam scores to answer Questions 7–9.

67 70 71 75 78 80 81 82 89 93 93

7. a. Find the mean. <u>79.9</u>

   b. Find the median. <u>80</u>

   c. Find the mode. <u>93</u>

   d. Which value does *not* represent the scores well? Explain why.

<u>Answers may vary. Sample: the mode; 9 of the 11 scores are lower</u>

<u>than the mode.</u>

8. Circle A, B, C or D. If the teacher gave an extra point to each student who scored below 80, which of the following would change?

   A. the high score   **B.** the mode

   C. the median   **(D.)** the mean

9. Circle A, B, C or D. Instead of adding an extra point, the teacher let everyone who scored below 80 take a re-test. If these students again scored below 80, which of these values would definitely *not* change?

   A. the low score   **B.** the mode

   (C.) the median   **D.** the mean

Two students in a driver education class asked to have their tests re-scored. One student had a score of 50, which was far below the class average. The other had a score of 70, which was close to the class average. Willard believes that adding 20 points to the lower score would raise the class average more than adding 20 points to the higher score.

10. To see if Willard is correct, you can use the strategy of solving a simpler problem. Suppose there are only five students in the class and their test scores are 50, 60, 70, 85, and 90.

   a. Find the class average. <u>71</u>

   b. Add 20 points to the score of 50. Keeping the other four original scores unchanged, find the new class average.

<u>75</u>

   c. Add 20 points to the score of 70. Keeping the other four original scores unchanged, find the new class average.

<u>75</u>

   d. Is Willard correct? Explain why or why not.

<u>No; adding 20 points to a low score has the same effect on the</u>

<u>mean as adding 20 points to a high score.</u>

11. The prices, in dollars, of nine homes in Smithville are given below.

    79,000   135,000   170,000   575,000   137,000
        148,000   153,000   79,000   110,000

    a. Find each of the following.

    the range <u>496,000</u>   the median <u>137,000</u>

    the mode <u>79,000</u>   the mean <u>176,222</u>

    b. Which value, the mean, the median, or the mode, best represents
    the prices of homes in Smithville? Explain your answer.

    <u>Answers may vary. Sample: the median; the other indicators are</u>

    <u>too low or too high.</u>

12. **Circle A, B, C, or D.**   Which of the following is the first step in
    finding the median of a set of numbers?

    A. Find the sum of the numbers.

    (B.) List the numbers in numerical order.

    C. Look for the most frequently occurring number.

    D. Divide each number by the number of terms.

13. **Circle A, B, C, or D.**   Fifteen student test scores are represented in
    the graph below. Find the mean, median, and mode of the scores.

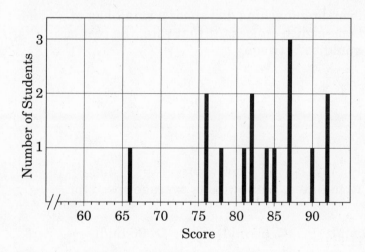

    (A.) mean = 83, median = 84, mode = 87

    B. mean = 84, median = 83, mode = 87

    C. mean = 83, median = 87, mode = 84

    D. mean = 84, median = 87, mode = 83

14. The profits or losses of five branches of a store are indicated in the table.

Store	Net Profit/Loss
1	+$365
2	+$492
3	−$225
4	+$849
5	+$320

Find the range of the data. $1,074

15. There are 20 students in a class. The average grade for that class on a test was computed as 74, but one student's grade was read mistakenly as 50 instead of 90. What will the average grade for that class be when it is recomputed using the corrected score?

76

Integrated Review

Circle A, B, C, or D.

16. For 45 cents, a snack-food vending machine dispenses a small bag of chips that weighs one and one-eighth ounces. At that rate, the cost of one pound of those chips would be between

  A. $2.30 and $2.75.

  B. $4.30 and $4.75.

  C. $6.30 and $6.75.

  D. $8.30 and $8.75.

17. A car traveled 8 miles in 12 minutes. What was its average speed for that trip?

  A. 1.5 mi/h   **B.** 40 mi/h   **C.** 60 mi/h   **D.** 96 mi/h

Lesson 4-2: Using Lists and Tables

Learn About It

When you use information from lists and tables, you need to consider only relevant information and ignore any unnecessary information.

Mrs. Wallenda lives in Fort Monmouth, NJ. She must catch a plane scheduled to leave Newark Airport at 12:20 P.M. She should get to the airport at least 40 minutes before her flight, but she refuses to wait at the airport any longer than necessary. Mrs. Wallenda considers the time table shown below to decide what bus she should take from Fort Monmouth.

Timetable: Departing Monmouth, Ocean, Union & Middlesex Counties
GOING TO: Newark International Airport

GOING TO NEWARK	Berkley Carteret Asbury Park	Fort Monmouth	Ramada West Long Branch	Sheraton Eatontown	Appletown Inn Eatontown	Marriot Residence Eatontown	Hilton Tinton Falls	Sunrise Suites Tinton Falls	Envoy Inn Tinton Falls	Bell Labs Red Hill-Holmdel	Hilton Woodbridge	Airline Shuttle	Ramada Inn Clark	Newark Airport	
AM		5:00	5:10	5:15	5:25	5:25	5:30	5:30	5:30	5:45	6:00	6:05	6:15	6:30	AM
AM	6:45	7:00	7:10	7:15	7:25	7:25	7:30	7:30	7:30	7:45	8:00	8:05	8:15	8:30	AM
AM	8:45	9:00	9:10	9:15	9:25	9:25	9:30	9:30	9:30	9:45	10:00	10:05	10:15	10:30	AM
AM	10:45	11:00	11:10	11:15	11:25	11:25	11:30	11:30	11:30	11:45	12:00	12:05	12:15	12:30	PM
PM	12:45	1:00	1:10	1:15	1:25	1:25	1:30	1:30	1:30	1:45	2:00	2:05	2:15	2:30	PM
PM	2:45	3:00	3:10	3:15	3:25	3:25	3:30	3:30	3:30	3:45	4:00	4:05	4:15	4:30	PM
PM	4:45	5:00	5:10	5:15	5:25	5:25	5:30	5:30	5:30	5:45	6:00	6:05	6:15	6:30	PM
PM	6:45	7:00	7:10	7:15	7:25	7:25	7:30	7:30	7:30	7:45	8:00	8:05	8:15	8:30	PM
PM	8:45	9:00	9:10	9:15	9:25	9:25	9:30	9:30	9:30	9:45	10:00	10:05	10:15	10:30	PM

1. What is the latest time Mrs. Wallenda should arrive at the airport?

11:40 A.M.

2. To find information about which bus Mrs. Wallenda should take, you need to look at only two columns of the time table, the Newark Airport column and the Fort Monmouth column.

a. What is the airport arrival time of the latest bus she can take?

10:30 A.M.

b. When does this bus depart from Fort Monmouth? 9:00 A.M.

3. Jorge is flying to Puerto Rico on a 9:15 A.M. flight. He must be at the airport two hours before his flight leaves. If Jorge is departing from Woodbridge, at what time should he get the bus?

6:00 A.M.

For a research project, Wanda collected information about students in her school. Her results are given in the partial list shown below.

Name	Gender (M or F)	Age (years)	Took Algebra in Eighth Grade (yes or no)
Adams, Steven	M	14	yes
Arias, Paula	F	15	yes
Belotti, Jake	M	14	no
Brudinsky, Belinda	F	16	no

Wanda wants to see if there is a relationship between gender and whether or not a student took algebra in eighth grade. Wanda is looking at the four tables shown below to see which would be the most helpful.

A.

Name	Algebra in 8th yes	no
Adams, Steven	X	
Arias, Paula	X	
Belotti, Jake		X
Brudinsky, Belinda		X

B.

	Average Age
male	14.1
female	13.7

C.

Algebra in 8th		Gender	
yes	no	male	female
343	219	289	273

D.

	Algebra in 8th yes	no
male	175	114
female	168	105

4. Does Wanda need to have the following information listed in her final table? Answer yes or no to each item.

a. names of the students   <u>no</u>

b. average age of the students   <u>no</u>

c. number of females who took algebra in the eighth grade   <u>yes</u>

d. number of males who took algebra in the eighth grade   <u>yes</u>

5. Which table contains the information that Wanda needs? Explain your answer.

<u>Table D; it has the number of students of each gender who did or did</u>

<u>not take algebra in eighth grade.</u>

The table below gives the average weekly income of people in the United States who are at least 25-years old.

Education Level	Average Weekly Income	
	Men	Women
high school not completed	$352	$250
high school completed	$472	$329
1 – 3 years of college	$563	$409
4 or more years of college	$766	$563

6. You want to use the table to find the difference between the average income of a woman who has completed four or more years of college and the average income of a man who has completed one to three years of college.

a. What is the average weekly income of a woman who has completed four or more years of college?

$563

b. What is the average weekly income of a man who has completed one to three years of college?

$563

c. What is the difference between the two incomes? $0

Apply What You've Learned

Mileage between Principal Cities	Atlantic City	Bridgeton	Camden	Cape May	Cherry Hill	Easton, PA	Elizabeth	Jersey City	Long Branch	Newark	New Brunswick	New York, NY	Paterson	Trenton
Atlantic City		81	57	48	55	115	105	119	83	108	93	130	123	74
Camden	57	40		84	9	57	81	85	81	84	56	104	99	32
Newark	108	116	84	154	80	66	8	6	48		23	27	15	50
Paterson	123	131	99	165	95	63	23	21	63	15	38	32		84
Trenton	74	70	32	106	35	52	48	56	48	50	28	74	84	
New Brunswick	93	99	56	128	58	45	26	31	40	23		46	38	28

7. Circle A, B, C, or D. Newark, NJ and Cape May, NJ are connected by major highways. Use the mileage chart shown above to find approximately how long it would take to drive from Newark to Cape May in traffic that averages 55 miles per hour.

A. $1\frac{1}{2}$ hours   **B.** 2 hours   **C.** 3 hours   **D.** 4 hours

8. Because of a printer malfunction, Ms. Raymond could not read some of the information on her checking account statement.

```
┌─────────────────────────────────────────────────────────────┐
│              CHECKING ACCOUNT SUMMARY                          │
│              ACCOUNT NO.  00-622-93-1                          │
│                                                                │
│    BEGINNING BALANCE  04/30/94 . . . . . . . . . . . $216.83  │
│    2 DEPOSITS/CREDITS . . . . . . . . . . . . . . . . xxxxxxx  │
│    3 CHECKS/DEBITS . . . . . . . . . . . . . . . . . . xxxxxxx │
│    SERVICE CHARGES . . . . . . . . . . . . . . . . . . xxxxxxx │
│    ENDING BALANCE  05/29/94 . . . . . . . . . . . . . xxxxxxx  │
│                                                                │
│           MISCELLANEOUS DEBITS AND CREDITS                     │
│    DATE      AMOUNT       DESCRIPTION        REFERENCE         │
│    05/01     10.09 −       SERVICE FEE       300003884         │
│    05/06     163.50 +      DEPOSIT           306095512         │
│    05/14     35.00 +       DEPOSIT           304422472         │
│                                                                │
│                  CHECKS PRESENTED                              │
│    DATE      AMOUNT       CHECK NUMBER       REFERENCE         │
│    05/11     300.00       1030               303359211         │
│    05/21     50.00        1032               305449288         │
│    05/26     13.54        1031               308750882         │
└─────────────────────────────────────────────────────────────┘
```

She needs to know the ending balance for that account as of 5/29/94. What was the ending balance?

$41.70

Integrated Review

Circle A, B, C, or D.

9. If you have a set of data containing 15 values, which one of the following will always be equal to one of the values in your set?

A. the mean
B. the range
C. the median
D. the number of values

10. In which list are the units of measure arranged in order from LEAST to GREATEST?

A. centimeter, meter, kilometer

B. meter, centimeter, kilometer

C. centimeter, kilometer, meter

D. meter, kilometer, centimeter

Lesson 4-3: Bar Graphs

Learn About It

You can use a bar graph to compare amounts.

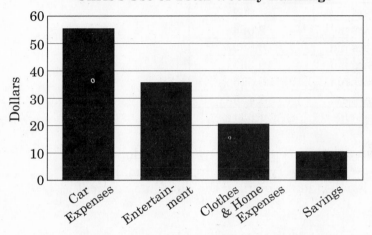

Chris's Use of Total Weekly Earnings

1. Chris wants to use the bar graph shown above to determine how much more he spends on entertainment each week than he saves.

   a. What does Chris spend on entertainment each week? <u>$35</u>

   b. What does Chris save each week? <u>$10</u>

   c. Find the difference. <u>$25</u>

Double bar graphs allow you to compare amounts within categories.

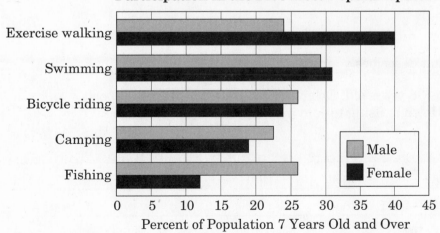

Participation in the Five Most Popular Sports

2. What sport is most popular with females? <u>**exercise walking**</u>

3. What sport is twice as popular with males as females? <u>**fishing**</u>

Data presented in a table is sometimes difficult to understand. You can make it easier to visualize the data by displaying it in a bar graph with either horizontal or vertical bars.

Volunteer Workers	
Age Range	Number (1,000)
Total	38,042
16 to 19 years old	1,902
20 to 24 years old	2,064
25 to 34 years old	8,680
35 to 44 years old	10,337
45 to 54 years old	5,670
55 to 64 years old	4,455
65 years and older	4,934

Helen is using the table shown above to convince her father to do volunteer work. Helen's argument is "Everyone is doing it." To make the data clearer to her father, Helen decides to display the data in a vertical bar graph.

5. Complete the following steps to create a bar graph of Helen's data using the grid provided at the top of the next page.

   a. How many bars will you need? __7 bars__

   b. Label the horizontal axis using the intervals in the table. Leave enough room to fit the number of bars you will need.

   c. Choose numbers for the vertical axis. Your numbers should start at zero and go higher than the highest value you need to graph. Be sure your numbers go up in equal *increments*, or steps.

   d. Label the vertical axis. Remember to indicate that the values are in thousands.

   e. Draw the bars and complete your graph.

   f. Add a title that describes your graph.

6. Helen's father is 38 years old. Do you think your bar graph supports the argument Helen is using to convince her father to volunteer? Why or why not?

   __Answers may vary. Sample: Helen's graph shows that many people__

   __her father's age are volunteering, which supports Helen's argument.__

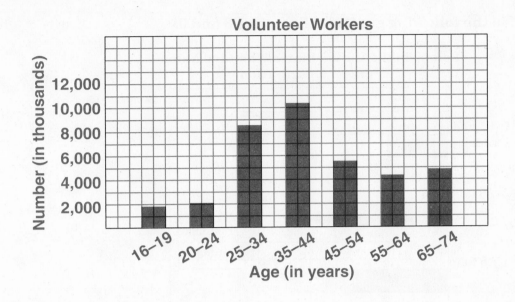

Volunteer Workers

Apply What You've Learned

7. Circle A, B, C, or D. The classes in a high school raised the amounts shown for a charity.

Class	Seniors	Juniors	Sophomores	Freshmen
Amount Raised	$235	$208	$215	$148

Four students started to construct a bar graph showing this information. Which of the following four approaches to beginning the graph is most likely to be easiest to interpret?

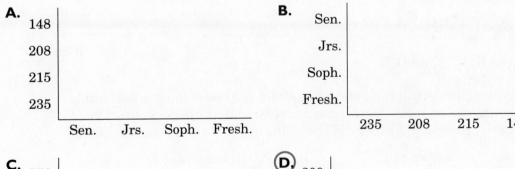

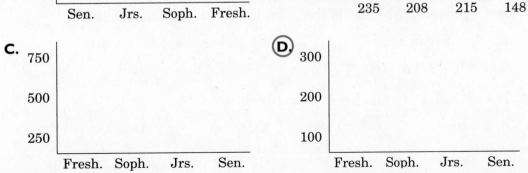

Use the following graph for Exercises 8 and 9.

People in the United States Who Live Alone
Percent Distribution

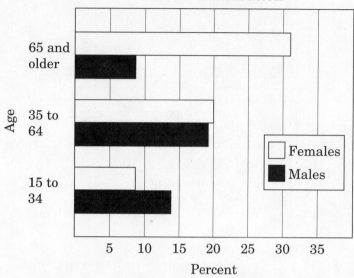

8. What percent of the population living alone is

   a. male, age 65 or older? <u>8%</u>

   b. female, age 15 to 34? <u>8%</u>

9. Describe the category of people who are most likely to live alone.
   Give an explanation for why more people in this category live alone
   than people in any other category.

   <u>Answers may vary. Sample: females over 65; women have a longer</u>

   <u>life expectancy than men.</u>

Integrated Review

Circle A, B, C, or D.

10. A teacher is compiling statistics about his class using a list that
    contains the name, age, home address, and grade point average of
    each student. Which one of the following could not be determined?

    A. the median age   **B.** the average family size

    C. the highest average   **D.** the oldest student

11. The diameter of a quarter is probably closest to

    A. 2.5 mm   **B.** 2.5 cm   **C.** 25 cm   **D.** 2.5 m

Lesson 4-4: Circle Graphs

Work Together

A circle graph displays data that represent parts of a whole. The circle graph shown below displays 1992 sales of recorded music by the type of music sold.

Percent of 1992 Music Sales by Type

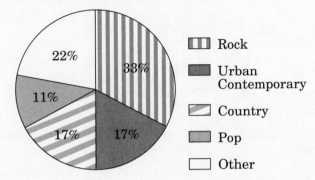

1. Which type of music had the highest percent of sales? <u>rock</u>

2. How many times greater was the sale of rock music than the sale of pop music?

   <u>3 times greater</u>

3. Which two types of music had the same percent of sales?

   <u>urban contemporary and country</u>

4. Which two types of music together accounted for more than half of all music sales?

   <u>rock and other</u>

Work together with a partner and survey your class or a group of your friends. Ask people which one of these five music categories they prefer.

5. Using your survey results, find the percent of people who prefer each type of music.

   <u>Answers may vary. Check students' work.</u>

6. Compare the results of your survey to the results given in the circle graph. Explain why your results are similar or different.

   <u>Answers may vary. Check students' work.</u>

Learn About It

Some circle graphs have values expressed as percents. Other circle graphs are labeled with the value of each part of the whole.

Example 1

The circle graph below displays the results of a school fund-raiser. Each section gives the number of candy bars sold by that class.

Candy Bars Sold by Class

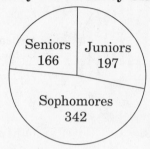

What percent of the sales were made by the senior class?

There are two ways to answer this question.

Method 1
Use the visual properties of the circle graph. The section representing seniors is a little less than one quarter of the circle. So the seniors made slightly less than 25% of the sales.

Method 2
For a more precise answer, divide the seniors' sales by the total sales.

$$166 \div 705 = 0.235460992$$

Rounding to the nearest percent, seniors made 24% of the sales.

Apply What You've Learned

Use the graph in Example 1 for Exercises 7 and 8.

7. Estimate the percent of sales made by juniors. <u>about 25%</u>

8. If the students made $.75 profit on each candy bar, how much profit did the sophomore class make?

<u>$256.50</u>

Use the following graph for Exercises 9–12.

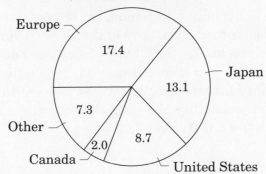

World Production of Cars
(in billions of cars)

Europe — 17.4

Japan — 13.1

7.3

Other

2.0

Canada

8.7

United States

9. What region produced more than one third of the world production of cars?

   <u>Europe</u>

10. How many times greater was car production in Europe than in the United States?

   <u>2 times greater</u>

11. About what percent of the world production of cars came from Japan?

   <u>about 27%</u>

12. Circle A, B, C, or D. How many more cars were produced in Japan than in the United States?

   A. 44,000,000   **B.** 4,040,000

   C. 4,400,000,000   **D.** 4,400,000

Integrated Review

Circle A, B, C, or D.

13. Suppose the 36 students in a junior class sold an average of 4.25 play tickets each. If each ticket to the play cost $4, how much money did the class bring in from their sale of tickets to the play?

   A. $144   **B.** $153

   C. $612   **D.** not enough information

14. Find the next term of the sequence 4, 5, 7, 10, 14, ...

   A. 17   **B.** 18   **C.** 19   **D.** 20

Lesson 4-5: Probability

Learn About It

The *probability* of an event is a number describing the chance that the event will occur. For example, consider the days of the week. If you choose a day at random, the probability that it is a Monday is 1 out of 7, or $\frac{1}{7}$. The probability that the day you choose begins with the letter T is 2 out of 7, or $\frac{2}{7}$. The probability that the day you choose has less than 15 letters is 7 out of 7, or 1. The probability of an impossible event, such as choosing a day with only 3 letters, is 0 out of 7, or 0.

Example 1

Each month, a high school does a feature newspaper article on one of its students who is picked at random. The number of male and female students in each grade is shown in the table.

Number of Students							
Grade 9		Grade 10		Grade 11		Grade 12	
M	F	M	F	M	F	M	F
28	30	31	29	25	26	25	23

What is the probability that the student chosen will be a female in grade 9?

The **probability** of an event occurring is the ratio of the favorable possibilities to the total number of possibilities. There are 30 female students in grade 9 and there are 217 students in the school.

The probability that a female in grade 9 is chosen is $\frac{30}{217}$. You can also express this probability as a decimal, about 0.14, or a percent, about 14%.

1. Consider the probability that a male in grades 11 or 12 is chosen.

   a. Find the number of males in grades 11 and 12. __50 males__

   b. Find the probability by finding the ratio of the number of males in grades 11 and 12 to the total number of students.
   $\frac{50}{217} \approx$ 0.23 or 23%

2. Find the probability that the student chosen is *not* in grade 10. (*Hint:* first find the number of students who are *not* in grade 10.)
   $\frac{157}{217} \approx$ 0.72 or 72%

You can also find probability in geometric problems.

Example 2

Which spinner would give you the best chance of spinning a three?

A.
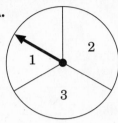

B.
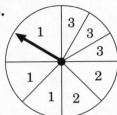

C.
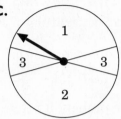

D.
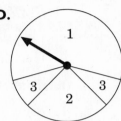

In each case, the probability of spinning a three is equal to the fraction representing the portion of the spinner where you can land on a three.

The probabilities are A: $\frac{1}{3}$, B: $\frac{1}{4}$, C and D: about $\frac{1}{6}$.

You would have the best chance of spinning a three with spinner A.

3. An empty room in a house is 16 feet long, 12 feet wide, and 8 feet high. A fly is equally likely to be in any part of the room. You want to find the probability that at a particular instant, the fly will be no more than one foot away from the ceiling.

   a. Find the volume of the portion of the room that is no more than one foot from the ceiling.

   192 ft³

   b. Find the volume of the room. 1,536 ft³

   c. Find the probability that the fly is no more than one foot from the ceiling by finding the ratio of the volume of the portion of the room to the volume of the whole room.
   $\frac{192}{1,536} = 0.125$ or 12.5%

Apply What You've Learned

Use the spinners from Example 2 to answer Exercises 4 and 5.

4. Which spinner would give you the best chance of spinning a one? D

5. What is the probability of spinning an odd number on spinner A? $\frac{2}{3} \approx 67\%$

6. Mr. Huber rewards his students by letting them draw a ticket from his "goodie" bag. The bag contains the following tickets.

3 tickets for a free cookie
2 tickets for 10% off at the Pizza Palace
5 tickets for a free ice cream
10 tickets for a congratulatory handshake

Kesha did all of her homework, so she gets to draw from the bag.

a. What is the probability she will win a free ice cream? $\frac{1}{4}$ **or 25%**

b. What is the probability that she will just get a handshake? $\frac{1}{2}$ **or 50%**

c. Kesha wants to improve her chances of winning a 10% discount at the Pizza Palace. Mr. Huber says he will allow her to add or remove three tickets before drawing from the bag. Describe two ways Kesha can add or remove tickets to improve her chances.

Answers may vary. Sample: Kesha can remove three free-cookie tickets or add three pizza-discount tickets.

7. A CD player is raffled off at a picnic. The tickets cost a dollar each, three for two dollars, or an arm's length for five dollars. An arm's length averages 21 tickets, depending on the arm of the seller. Suppose 600 tickets were sold before the drawing and you bought five arm's lengths. What is the probability that you will win?

if you have average arms, $\frac{105}{600}$ **or 17.5%**

8. A very small stone is somewhere in a bucket of sawdust. The weight of the sawdust by itself is 50 ounces. If a full scoop holds five ounces of sawdust, what is the probability of getting that stone by taking two full scoops of sawdust out of the bucket?

$\frac{1}{5}$ **or 20%**

Integrated Review

Circle A, B, C, or D.

9. On a five-hour trip, Mary traveled at an average speed of 20 mi/h for the first hour and an average speed of 50 mi/h for the next four hours. What was her average speed for those five hours?

A. 35 mi/h   **B.** 44 mi/h   **C.** 70 mi/h   **D.** 40 mi/h

10. Find the area of a right triangle with sides 3 cm, 4 cm, and 5 cm.

A. 6 cm^2 **B.** 10 cm^2 **C.** 12 cm^2 **D.** 20 cm^2

Lesson 4-6: Making Predictions

Work Together

When you roll a die, the probability of rolling a 2 is $\frac{1}{6}$, or about 17%. If you roll a die repeatedly, you might predict that a 2, or any one of the other five numbers, will come up about 17% of the time. Perform the following experiment with your partner to see what actually happens.

Roll a die six times while your partner records the results. Then switch and record the data while your partner rolls six times. Record your results for the 12 rolls in the second column of the table. Then complete the third column by finding the percent of the time each of the numbers occurred in the 12 rolls.

Answers will vary. Check students' work.

Number on Die	Data from you and your partner		Data from the entire class	
	Number of Occurrences	Percent of Total	Number of Occurrences	Percent of Total
1				
2				
3				
4				
5				
6				

1. Describe how your results compare with the prediction.

Answers may vary. Check students' work.

Since you only rolled the die a total of 12 times, your results may be very different from the prediction. Now combine your results with the results of the other groups in your class. Use the class results to complete the last two columns of the table.

2. Describe how the class results compare with the prediction.

Answers may vary, but should be close.

3. If your experiment involved 400 rolls, do you think your results would be closer to the prediction? Explain why or why not.

Answers may vary. Sample: yes; the more rolls, the closer the results will be to the prediction.

Learn About It

A **sample** is a small group that is used to make predictions about a larger group. In order for a sample to be useful, it must be randomly selected and large enough to represent the larger group.

Example 1

While interviewing students at Washington High School, Paul asked 20 students, picked at random, what their favorite fall sport is. Maria picked 50 different students at random and asked them the same question. George combined Paul's data and Maria's data. All three graphed their results.

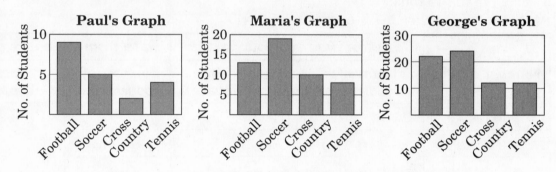

Use the most reliable graph to predict how many of the 725 students at the school would choose soccer as their favorite fall sport.

George's graph is the most reliable graph because it represents the largest sample of randomly selected students. George's graph indicates that 24 out of 70 students prefer soccer. To predict the total number of students in the school who prefer soccer, solve the following proportion.

$\frac{24}{70} = \frac{x}{725}$

$x = 725 \boxed{\times} 24 \boxed{\div} 70 = 248.5714286$

About 249 students would choose soccer as their favorite fall sport.

4. Predict the number of students who would choose tennis as their favorite fall sport.

<u>about 124 students</u>

5. If Maria had collected her data at a soccer game, do you think this would affect the predictions? Explain why or why not.

<u>Answers may vary. Sample: yes; students at a soccer game are more</u>

<u>likely to choose soccer than students chosen at random.</u>

Apply What You've Learned

6. Your best friend is running for class president. As campaign manager, you take a poll of all of your friends at lunch. Explain why this is *not* a good sample.

<u>Answers may vary. Sample: your friends may be likely to share your</u>

<u>opinions.</u>

7. You toss a coin three times and it comes up heads each time. Do you think that this is a two-headed coin? Explain why or why not.

<u>Answers may vary. Sample: no; there are not enough trials to indicate</u>

<u>whether the coin is two-headed or not.</u>

8. Student Council takes a poll to see how many students wear hats during the school day. In Tom's homeroom of 30 freshmen, 12 students wear hats. In DeWayne's homeroom of 25 sophomores, 10 students wear hats. In Marla's homeroom of 23 juniors, 15 students wear hats. In Florissa's homeroom of 26 seniors, 18 students wear hats. There are 1252 students in the school. Based on this sample information, predict the total number of students who wear hats.

<u>662 students</u>

9. To estimate the number of fish in a pond, Jake tagged the 45 fish that he caught. Then he threw the fish back into the pond. On the next day, Jake caught 20 fish and found tags on 2 of them. Predict the number of fish in the pond based on Jake's sample.

<u>450 fish</u>

Integrated Review

Circle A, B, C, or D.

10. What is the probability of rolling a multiple of three when you roll a die one time?

   A. $\frac{1}{2}$ **B.** $\frac{1}{3}$ **C.** $\frac{1}{6}$ **D.** $\frac{2}{3}$

11. A medium-size school bus can transport no more than 28 passengers. If each bus makes only one trip, what is the smallest number of medium-size school buses that is enough to transport 377 students from one place to another?

   A. 13   **B.** 13.5   **C.** 14   **D.** 14.5

Lesson 4-7: Interpreting Graphs

Learn About It

Some graphs show how two quantities relate to one another. You can interpret one of these graphs by looking at where it increases, where it decreases, and where it levels off.

Example 1

The graph at the right shows the distance Marisabel traveled as she drove to her aunt's house. During which half-hour interval was Marisabel most likely traveling on a highway? During which half-hour interval did Marisabel most likely stop for something to eat?

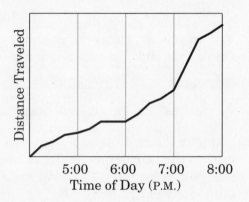

The graph relates the time of day to the distance traveled. To find when Marisabel was most likely on a highway, find the portion of the graph where the distance traveled increased the fastest. This occurred between 7:00 and 7:30 P.M., where the graph is steepest.

To find the period of time when Marisabel most likely stopped for something to eat, find the portion of the graph where the distance traveled did not increase. This occurred between 5:30 and 6:00 P.M., where the graph is level.

Each of the following graphs relates the age of a car to its resale value.

A.

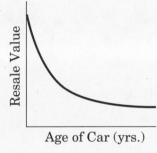

B.

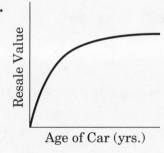

C.

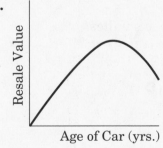

D.

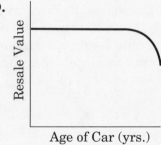

---

1. Answer the following questions to determine which graph correctly shows the relationship between the age of a car and its resale value.

a. If you buy a car, does its value increase or decrease with time?

<u>decrease</u>

b. Based on your answer to part (a) which two graphs *cannot* possibly be correct?

<u>B, C</u>

c. Look at the two remaining graphs. Consider whether the value of a car remains about the same for a few years or whether the value changes steadily. With this in mind, choose the graph that best relates the age of a car to its resale value.

<u>A</u>

Apply What You've Learned

2. Circle A, B, C, or D. Mrs. Nelson knows that she will have 18 students in her homeroom. She draws a graph to illustrate the possible distribution of boys and girls. Which of the following graphs did Mrs. Nelson draw? (*Hint:* Remember that the number of students always remains the same.)

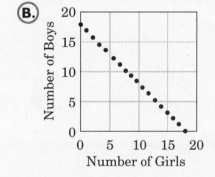

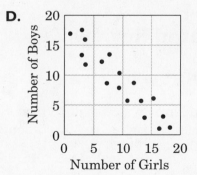

3. Circle A, B, C, or D. The graph indicates the distance traveled by two marathoners, Elsa and Kendra. The women started running at the same time. What can you conclude from the graph?

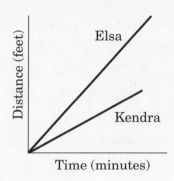

A. Elsa ran up a steeper hill than Kendra.

B. Elsa ran faster than Kendra.

C. Kendra ran faster than Elsa.

D. Kendra ran up a steeper hill than Elsa.

Use the following map for Exercise 4.

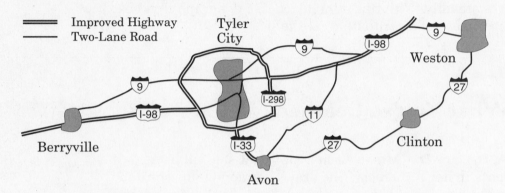

4. Circle A, B, or C. Which graph below most likely corresponds to a person's Saturday automobile trip from Berryville to Clinton by way of I-98, I-298, I-33, and Route 27?

A.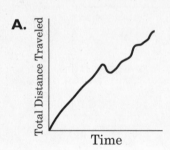

B.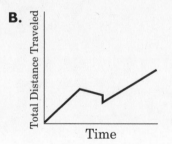

C.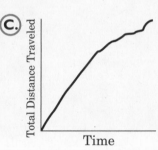

Integrated Review

Circle A, B, C, or D.

5. Two students in a class of 18 have red hair. Predict the total number of redheads if there are 360 students in the school.

    A. 9   **B.** 18   **C.** 20   **D.** 40

6. Find the perimeter of a square with area 625 cm^2.

    A. 25 cm   **B.** 50 cm   **C.** 100 cm   **D.** 312.5 cm

Lesson 4-8: Choosing an Appropriate Graph

Learn About It

You can display data in many different ways. The graph you choose depends upon the type of information you have.

The following graphs display data about enrollment at Central School.

Central School Enrollment

Number of Students

600
500
400
300
200
100

Girls
Boys

10   11   12
Grade

Central School Enrollment

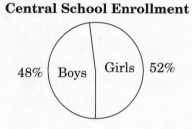

48%   Boys   Girls   52%

Central School Enrollment

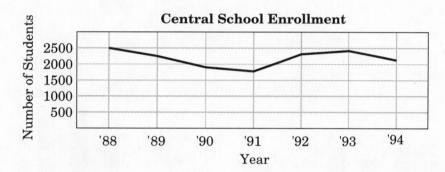

Number of Students

2500
2000
1500
1000
500

'88   '89   '90   '91   '92   '93   '94
Year

1. Which grade has the most boys? __12__

2. Are there more boys or girls at Central School? __girls__

3. Between which two years did the greatest increase in Central School enrollment occur?

__1991 and 1992__

4. Look back at Questions 1–3. Which questions did you answer using the circle graph? the double bar graph? the line graph?

__Question 2; Question 1; Question 3__

The circle graph compares parts of a whole, the double bar graph compares data for different groups, and the line graph displays data that changes continuously over time.

Example 1

Which of the following graphs would be most useful in solving the problem in the box?

> On Thursday, John, Bernice and Carmen took a train from Baltimore to New York. The train left Baltimore at 1:00 P.M. and arrived in New York City at 4:30 P.M. For the first 45 minutes of the trip, John was reading; he slept for the last half hour of the trip. During the trip, Bernice read from 1:30 P.M. to 2:30 P.M. While riding on the train, Carmen started a crossword puzzle at 2:00 P.M., and stopped working on it an hour and a quarter later. How much time did John, Bernice, and Carmen have free to play cards together during the train ride?

A.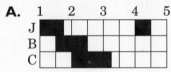

B.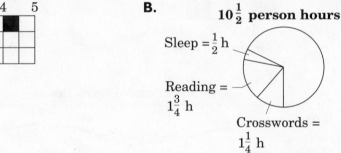

C.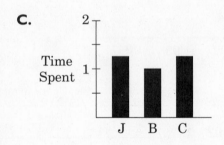

D.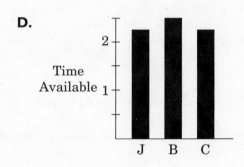

The answer is A. All four graphs present the information correctly, but only A gives you enough information to solve the problem.

Apply What You've Learned

5. Use graph A to solve the problem in the box in Example 1. <u>45 minutes</u>

6. Write a question that you could answer using graph B.

<u>Answers may vary. Check students' work.</u>

Enrollment in Public and Private Schools (in thousands)

SCHOOL	1970	1980	1990	2000 (projected)
Total	59,838	58,306	59,931	68,098
Public	52,322	50,335	51,767	58,759
Private	7,516	7,971	8,165	9,339
Grade K–8	36,610	31,639	33,808	37,548
Public	32,558	27,647	29,742	33,032
Private	4,052	3,992	4,162	4,516
Grade 9–12	14,647	14,570	12,413	14,858
Public	13,336	13,231	11,284	13,507
Private	1,311	1,339	1,129	1,351

Use the data shown above for Exercises 7–10. In each exercise, describe the type of graph you would draw.

7. to show the breakdown of the total 1970 enrollment into public and private school students

circle graph

8. to see how total school enrollment changes from 1970 to 2000

line graph

9. to compare K–8, 9–12, and total enrollment for public and private schools in 1990

double bar graph

10. Circle A, B, C, or D. There are five teams in a volleyball league. Every team plays every other team exactly once. Which one of the following figures would help determine the number of games played?

A. **B.** **C.** **D.**

Integrated Review

Circle A, B, C, or D.

11. Each week you put your allowance and some baby-sitting money in the bank. A graph that relates the total you saved to time would be

A. up and down   **B.** level   **C.** increasing   **D.** decreasing

12. Find the value of the next term of the sequence $3^2, 3^1, 3^0, \ldots.$

A. -3 **B.** $\frac{1}{3}$ **C.** -1 **D.** 0

Lesson 4-9: Answering Open-Ended Questions

Work Together

You can work with a partner to improve your skills at answering open-ended questions. First work individually to answer the following question.

1. The annual salaries of all of the employees of a small company are listed below.

   President: $110,000

   Vice-president: $60,000

   Senior Professionals: $50,000 $48,000 $48,000 $44,000

   Junior Professionals: $36,000 $36,000 $36,000 $32,000

   Clerical Staff: $22,000 $18,000 $14,000

   What are the mean, the median, and the mode of the salaries of the employees of this company? How is each of these statistics affected if one excludes the president's salary? What do your findings tell you about the statistic that should probably be used in discussions of the salary of a typical baseball player? Explain.   **Check students' work.**

2. The scoring guide on the following page explains exactly how answers are scored. Exchange work with your partner and use the scoring guide to score each other's answer.

   Score: <u>**Answers will vary. Check students' work.**</u>

Learn About It

Here are two sample responses.   **Answers may vary. Samples given.**

Sample 1

Mean: $42,615
Median: $36,000
Mode: $36,000

If you take out the president, the mean drops to $37,000 but the mode and median stay the same.

Usually the better you are in baseball the more you make, so its hard to tell!

3. This response scored a **2**. Explain why. <u>The response does not indicate that the median or mode is better than the mean in this case.</u>

Sample 2

```
110,000                42,615.50        Mean – $42,615.50
 60,000            13) 554,000          Median – $36,000
 50,000                                 Mode – $36,000
 48,000 ⎤
 48,000 ⎦ 2
 44,000
→ 36,000 ⎤              The average or mean
 36,000 ⎬ 3             would be affected.
 36,000 ⎦
 32,000
 22,000
 18,000
 14,000
─────────
554,000
```

4. This response scored a **1**. Explain why. <u>The mean, median, and mode are</u>
<u>correct, but the rest of the question is not answered adequately.</u>

5. Look back at your answer to Question 1. If you did not score a **3**, use
what you have learned to write an improved answer.
Check students' work.

Apply What You've Learned

6. The math exam scores for the 21 students in Mr. Walker's class were:

$$65 \quad 90 \quad 82 \quad 78 \quad 84 \quad 92 \quad 88 \quad 86 \quad 70 \quad 68 \quad 75$$
$$88 \quad 90 \quad 85 \quad 61 \quad 81 \quad 79 \quad 82 \quad 84 \quad 83 \quad 90$$

a. The mean or average of the above scores is 81. What is the median score? What is the mode?

b. Use the grid shown below to make a bar graph showing the frequency or the number of scores in each of the score ranges 60–64, 65–69, 70–74, etc.

c. What is the best general indicator of the class's performance on the exam – the mean, the median, or the mode? Explain your answer.

Rank ordered scores are:
61 65 68 70 75 78 79
81 82 82 83 84 84 85
86 88 88 90 90 90 92

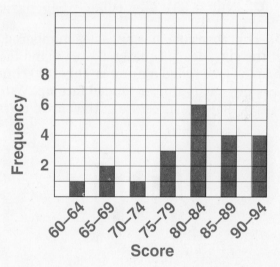

SCORING GUIDE:

3 Student answers (a) correctly (median – 83, mode – 90), presents an accurate graph for (b), and chooses the median as the best general indicator for (c), **AND** work is clear.

2 Student answers (a), (b), and (c) correctly but work is unclear **OR** answers (a) and (b) correctly but (c) is incorrect, work is clear **OR** answers (a), (b), and/or (c) incorrectly due to minor computational errors, work is clear.

1 Student answers (a), (b), and (c) incorrectly due to minor computational errors **OR** answers parts of (a), (b), and (c) correctly but work missing.

0 The student answers inappropriately or fails to attempt an answer.

Circle A, B, C, or D.

1. There are 17 boys and 19 girls in your economics class. Suppose a student is chosen at random. Find the probability that the student chosen is a girl.

   A. $\frac{1}{17}$ **B.** $\frac{1}{2}$ **C.** $\frac{1}{19}$ **(D.)** $\frac{19}{36}$

2. During one hour, the amounts withdrawn from an automatic teller machine were $20, $40, $70, $10, $40, $100, $80, and $50. Find the mean, median, and mode of these withdrawals.

   A. mean = $45, median = $40, mode = $40

   B. mean = $40, median = $50, mode = $50.25

   C. mean = $51.25, median = $40, mode = $100

   (D.) mean = $51.25, median = $45, mode = $40

3. A number cube has six sides numbered from one to six. Any one of the six sides is equally likely to land face up. Suppose each student in a class rolled a number cube 100 times and recorded how many times each number landed face up. Which graph below most likely represents the results of the entire class?

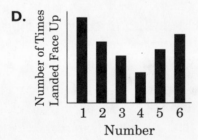

4. South Memorial High School has 745 students. A sample of 40 students is picked at random. Of the 40 students, 17 play a musical instrument. Use this sample to predict the number of students in the school who play a musical instrument.

   A. about 43   **(B.)** about 317

   C. about 680   **D.** about 1,753

5. Suppose an oven is turned on and set for a certain temperature. Which one of the graphs below relates the temperature of the oven to the length of time it is on?

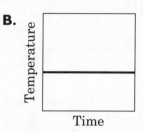

A.

B.

C.

D.

6. Amanda earns $6.50/h for the time she works Monday through Friday and $7.50/h on weekends. Her time card is shown below.

Employee Time Card						
Name: Amanda Black				**Date:** 11/30/96		
Day:	Mon	Tues	Wed	Thurs	Fri	Sat	Sun
Hours:	4.5	3.5	6	7.5	0	4	3.5

How much did Amanda earn for that week?

A. $147.50   **B.** $188.50   **C.** $196.00   **D.** $244.75

7. Scientists have found that there are two different types of sleep. The graph below compares the number of hours of each type of sleep for people of different ages. About how many times as much non-REM sleep as REM sleep does a three-year-old get?

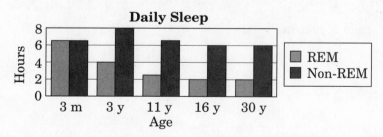

A. about half as much   **B.** about twice as much

C. about the same   **D.** about three times as much

8. The table below shows the test scores of the students who took their written driver's test at a particular testing center one day.

Name	School	Score
Adams, J.	Gunnison	62
Baker, P.	Taylor	76
Chin, H.	Gunnison	87
Drabowski, C.	Braddock	79
Elmore, J.	Taylor	64
Ferris, W.	Braddock	83
Garver, G.	Gunnison	81
Greer, P.	Braddock	84
Harris, R.	Gunnison	92

Name	School	Score
Jacoby, P.	Taylor	92
Kelly, M.	Braddock	88
Lassiter, L.	Braddock	94
Martin, S.	Gunnison	82
Petrocelli, R.	Gunnison	74
Ramirez, R.	Taylor	84
Saunders, M.	Taylor	80
Thompson, L.	Braddock	89
Wilson, P.	Gunnison	90

All of these students participated in the driver-education program offered at his or her own high school. Based on the students' test scores, which school's driver-education program appears to prepare its students best for the written driver's test?

A. Braddock

B. Taylor

C. Gunnison

D. Two schools appear to prepare their students equally well.

9. To find out if a particular area is generally above or below sea level, a geologist checked the elevation at several places in the area. She obtained the following results relative to sea level measured to the nearest foot; positive numbers represent distance above sea level and negative numbers represent distance below sea level.

$$+3, +5, -3, +1, -4, -2, +1, -3, -4, -4$$

What is the area's average elevation?

A. -10 ft

B. -1 ft

C. 0 ft

D. $+10$ ft

Write your answer in the boxes at the top of the grid, one number (or decimal point) per box. Then fill in the corresponding circle below each box.

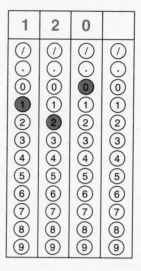

10. Use the circle graph below. If 48 people in the survey were undecided, how many people surveyed were against Amendment 5?

Survey on Amendment 5

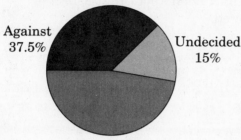

Against 37.5%

Undecided 15%

For 47.5%

Answer the following open-ended question in the space below.

11. Suppose you have a part-time job at Burger Paradise. When you start your four-hour shift at 4:00 P.M., your cash register contains $50. Draw a graph which reasonably represents the amount of money in your cash register as you work through your entire shift. Carefully explain what your graph shows and why. You will be graded on the basis of the reasonableness and clarity of your graph and on the quality of your thinking and your explanation.

Graphs may vary.
A sample is given.

SCORING GUIDE:

3 Reasonable bar graph, step function, isolated parts, or line graph (with axes labeled for time and money) **AND** explanation of slow-fast-slow increase in cash in register consistent with graph

2 Flawed graph with reasonable explanation consistent with graph **OR** acceptable graph with poor or inconsistent explanation

1 Acceptable graph with no or unsatisfactory explanation **OR** reasonable explanation with no or unacceptable graph (e.g., linear)

0 Unacceptable graph and unacceptable explanation **OR** blank or other irrelevant response

Alternative Assessment Projects

Here are some projects that will demonstrate your understanding of the topics in this chapter.

Project 1

Using several different brands of a product (backpacks, cereals, potato chips, or sneakers, for example), design a method for comparing some aspect of the product. Use your method to gather information, then organize your information and reach a conclusion about that aspect of the product based on the data you collected.

SCORING GUIDE:

3 The student develops some appropriate questions, gathers data, and organizes the data using a table, chart, or graph that is used to reach a conclusion.

2 The student develops some appropriate questions, gathers data, and attempts to organize the data using a table, chart, or graph but fails to reach a conclusion.

1 The student develops some appropriate questions and gathers some data.

0 The student answers inappropriately or fails to attempt an answer.

Project 2

Work with a group of students to design and conduct a statistical survey. Find the mean, median, and mode of your data.

SCORING GUIDE:

3 The student develops a survey with appropriate questions, gathers data, and analyzes it by calculating the mean, median, and mode. (Minor calculation errors are acceptable.)

2 The student develops a survey with appropriate questions, and gathers data but either fails to calculate one or two statistics or calculates them inappropriately.

1 The student participates in survey development and data collection but either fails to calculate the statistics or calculates them all inappropriately.

0 The student answers inappropriately or fails to attempt an answer.

Lesson 5-1: Evaluating Expressions

Work Together

Work with a partner to explore the *order of operations*. The **order of operations** is a set of rules for evaluating expressions that guarantees everyone gets the same answer.

Order of Operations

1. Do all operations within parentheses first.

2. Do all work with exponents.

3. Multiply and divide in order from left to right.

4. Add and subtract in order from left to right.

Have one member of your group use paper and pencil to evaluate the odd exercises and the other a scientific calculator (don't forget the order of the operations). Compare your answers. Swap roles for the even exercises.

1. $6 + 2(4)$ <u>**14**</u>   **2.** $15(-4) \div 3$ <u>**−20**</u>   **3.** $5(23 - 9)$ <u>**70**</u>

4. $(-3)^2$ <u>**9**</u>   **5.** -3^2 <u>**−9**</u>   **6.** $(2 + 3)^3$ <u>**125**</u>

7. $2^2 + 3^3$ <u>**31**</u>   **8.** $\sqrt{9 + 25}$ <u>**6**</u>   **9.** $\sqrt{9} + \sqrt{16}$ <u>**7**</u>

10. $2^4 - 4^3 \div 16 + (-4^2)$ <u>**28**</u>   **11.** $\left(\frac{3}{4}\right)^2 - \left(\frac{1}{2}\right)^5$ <u>**$\frac{17}{32}$**</u>

12. $17 - 3^2 + 6(7 - 3) - (-3)$ <u>**35**</u>
Remind students that they will need to use the parentheses keys for certain exercises.

Learn About It

You can evaluate a variable expression by replacing the variable with a number. Then follow the order of operations.

Example 1

Evaluate $3x^2 + 9$ when $x = -5$.

$3x^2 + 9 = 3(-5)^2 + 9$	**Replace x with −5.**
$= 3(25) + 9$	**Do all work with exponents.**
$= 75 + 9$	**Multiply.**
$= 84$	**Add.**

13. Would the value of the expression be the same if $x = 5$? Explain.

<u>Yes; $5^2 = (-5)^2$</u>

You can also use a scientific calculator to evaluate expressions.

Example 2

Evaluate $-x^2 + 9$ for $x = 0.3$.

$\boxed{\cdot}$ 3 $\boxed{x^2}$ $\boxed{+/-}$ $\boxed{+}$ 9 $\boxed{=}$ 8.91   **Input these keystrokes into your calculator.**

14. Explain how the keystrokes would change if you evaluated the expression using the $\boxed{y^x}$ key.

    The keystroke $\boxed{y^x}$ 2 $\boxed{=}$ would replace $\boxed{x^2}$.

15. Explain how to use the order of operations to evaluate the expression.

    Square 0.3, then take the opposite, then add 9.

You may need to evaluate expressions to determine the correct answer to a multiple choice question.

Example 3

If $x = 5$ which of the following expressions does NOT equal 25?

A. x^2 **B.** $-x^2$

C. $(-x)(-x)$ **D.** $(-x)^2$

Evaluate each expression for $x = 5$. Identify the expression not equal to 25.

A. $x^2 = 5^2 = 25$ **B.** $-x^2 = -5^2 = -(5^2) = -(25) = -25$

C. $(-x)(-x) = (-5)(-5) = 25$ **D.** $(-x)^2 = (-5)^2 = (-5)(-5) = 25$

The expression $-x^2$ is not equal to 25 when $x = 5$. B is the correct choice.

Apply What You've Learned

Use the order of operations to evaluate each of the following expressions. Let $x = 4$.

16. $2x^2$ __32__

17. $2x^2 - 3$ __29__

18. $-2x^2$ __−32__

19. $(-2x)^2$ __64__

20. $-x^2 + 5x + 1$ __5__

21. $3x^3 - 2x^2 + 10x - 4$ __196__

Evaluate each expression.

22. $3x^2 - 4x + 5$ for $x = 2$ $\underline{9}$

23. $3x^2 - 4x + 5$ for $x = -2$ $\underline{25}$

24. $5x^3 - 3x^2 + 2x - 7$ for $x = 1$ $\underline{-3}$

25. $5x^3 - 3x^2 + 2x - 7$ for $x = -1$ $\underline{-17}$

26. $(x + 4)$ for $x = -3$ $\underline{1}$

27. $(2x + 1)(3x - 40)$ for $x = 5$ $\underline{-275}$

28. $6x^5 - 4x$ for $x = 0.02$ $\underline{-0.07999998}$

29. $3x^2 - 4x + \frac{1}{3}$ for $x = \frac{1}{3}$ $\underline{-\frac{2}{3}}$

30. $(6 - x)^3$ for $x = -1.5$ $\underline{421.875}$

31. $6^3 - x^3$ for $x = -1.5$ $\underline{219.375}$

32. $(3x - 1)(3x + 1)$ for $x = -\frac{1}{4}$ $\underline{-\frac{7}{16}}$

33. $x^4 - 3x^2 + 5x - 2$ for $x = 1\frac{1}{2}$ $\underline{3\frac{13}{16}}$

34. Circle A, B, C, or D. Which expression has a value closest to 176?

    A. $11.5 \times 14 + 25.5$ **B.** $(6.2 \times 3)^2 \div 2$

    C. $7.5 + 3 \times 50$ **D.** $(35 \times 2.5 + 300) \div 2$

35. Circle A, B, C, or D. If $x = -3$, which of the following expressions does NOT equal 18?

    A. $2x^2$ **B.** $2(-x)^2$

    C. $-6x$ **D.** $-2x^2$

Integrated Review

Circle A, B, C, or D.

36. Five out of fifteen people responded to a questionnaire. How many people did not respond?

    A. 10   **B.** 5   **C.** 20   **D.** 15

37. What is the units digit of the twenty-first term of the sequence below?

$$7^1, 7^2, 7^3, \ldots, 7^n, \ldots$$

    A. 9   **B.** 7   **C.** 3   **D.** 1

Lesson 5-2: Variable Expressions

Work Together

Work with a partner to identify whether each term or word phrase implies the operation of addition, subtraction, multiplication, or division.

1. twice a number _mult._

2. perimeter _add._

3. 5 less than x _subtr._

4. the quotient of 8 and m _div._

5. 3 yd shorter then l _subtr._

6. 6 more than a number _add._

7. squared _mult._

8. area _mult._

Learn About It

You can translate a word phrase into a variable expression. This is very helpful when solving problems using algebra. You can use any letter to represent an unknown value.

Word Phrase	Variable Expression
eleven more than a number	$x + 11$
two less than four times a quantity	$4q - 2$
seven less than half of n	$\frac{1}{2}n - 7$
the sum of a number and its square	$n + n^2$

9. Draw a line from each word phrase in the first column to its corresponding variable expression in the second column.

A. five more than three times a number

B. the product of a number and -5

C. a number divided by three

D. twice a number divided by three

E. 3 less than five times a quantity

I. $\frac{x}{3}$

II. $5x - 3$

III. $\frac{2x}{3}$

IV. $3x + 5$

V. $-5x$

10. Write a variable expression for each word phrase. Use any variable.

a. nine less than twice a number $2n - 9$

b. four more than the square of a number $n^2 + 4$

11. The word phrases below represent three different variable expressions. The example to the right of each phrase uses the number 10.

    I. subtract twice the number from four times itself $4(10) - 2(10) = 20$

    II. three times the number plus its opposite $3(10) + (-10) = 20$

    III. four times the number divided by -2 $4(10) \div (-2) = -20$

  a. Write a variable expression in simplified form for each procedure. Use x for the variable. The first one is completed for you.

    I. $\underline{4x - 2x = 2x}$

    II. $\underline{3x + (-x) = 2x}$

    III. $\underline{4x \div (-2) = -2x}$

  b. Evaluate each variable expression for $x = 5$. Which expressions give equal results?

    $\underline{10;\ 10;\ -10;\ \text{I and II}}$

  c. How could you determine which expressions give equal results without evaluating for a given number?

    Answers may vary. Sample: Simplify the expressions

You can use a variable expression to represent the perimeter and area of a figure.

12. The length of a rectangle is twice as long as the width. The width of the rectangle is w.

$2w$

w

  a. A sketch of the rectangle is shown above. Label the width as w.

  b. Write a variable expression for the length of the rectangle.

    $2w$

  c. Label the length on the sketch.   **Check students' work.**

  d. Write a variable expression for the perimeter. Simplify.

    $2w + 2(2w) = 6w$

  e. Write a variable expression for the area. Simplify.

    $2w(w) = 2w^2$

You can use a variable expression to represent a situation.

13. Suppose a ball is dropped from a height of 10 ft and each time the ball bounces it goes up $\frac{1}{2}$ the distance it fell.

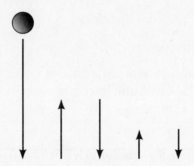

   a. Using the diagram above, what is the total distance the ball will have traveled when it hits the floor for the first time? the second time? the third time?

   <u>10 ft; 20 ft; 25 ft</u>

   b. What is the total distance the ball will travel when it hits the floor for the fourth time?

   <u>27.5 ft</u>

   c. Suppose the ball is dropped from a height of x ft. Write a variable expression to represent the total distance the ball will travel when it hits the floor for the fourth time.

   <u>2.75x ft</u>

Apply What You've Learned

14. Manuel is giving Davis lottery tickets for his birthday. He told Davis that he could choose from the following amounts.

     I. five times his age less twice his age

     II. his age increased by three times his age

     III. ten times his age minus eight times his age

Which amount should Davis choose? Support your answer.

<u>Answers may vary. Sample: II; this has the largest variable</u>

<u>expression, 4x of the three options.</u>

15. One leg of a right triangle is four times as long as the other leg. The length of the shorter leg is s.

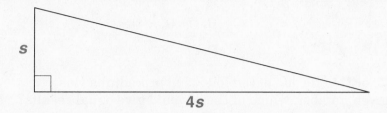

s

$4s$

   a. A sketch of the triangle is shown above. Label the length of the shorter leg as s.   **Check students' work.**

   b. Write a variable expression for the length of the longer leg.

       $4s$

   c. Label the length of the longer leg on the sketch.   **Check students' work.**

   d. Write a variable expression for the area of the triangle. Simplify.
       $\frac{1}{2}(4s)(s) = 2s^2$

16. At a local department store, 2 out of every 15 items purchased are returned, on the average.

   a. Fifteen purchased items are represented below. Cross out the items that are returned. Then, circle the items that are not returned.

   b. What fraction of the items are not returned? $\frac{13}{15}$

   c. Does the numerical expression $\frac{15-2}{15}$ represent the fraction of items that are not returned? Explain.

       Answers may vary. Sample: yes; subtracting the items returned

       from the total gives the items not returned.

   d. Suppose 2 items out of every x items purchased are returned, on the average. Write a variable expression to represent the fraction of items that are not returned.
       $\frac{x-2}{x}$

17. Circle A, B, C, or D. The length of a rectangular pool is l yards, and its width is 4 yards shorter than its length. Which of the following is an expression for the perimeter of that pool?

A. $2l + 2(l - 4)$ **B.** $l + (l - 4)$

C. $2l + 2(l + 4)$ **D.** $2l - 8$

18. Circle A, B, C, or D. If each of the following procedures was applied to a given number, which of them would give equal results?

    I. subtract twice the number from itself

    II. divide one by the number

    III. multiply the number by -1

A. I and II   **B.** II and III

C. I and III   **D.** I, II, and III

19. Circle A, B, C, or D. Which variable expression describes the area of the shaded region in the diagram ?

A. $a^2 + 16$

B. $64 - a^2$

C. $a^2 - 64$

D. $64 - 2a$

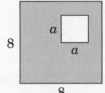

Integrated Review

Circle A, B, C, or D.

20. If $x = -2$, which of the following expressions does NOT equal 16?

A. x^4 **B.** $4x^2$ **C.** $-(-x)^4$ **D.** $-2x^3$

21. Which of the following statements is false?

A. A nonrectangular parallelogram and a rectangle can have the same area.

B. Two rectangles with the same area always have the same perimeter.

C. You can divide a parallelogram into two congruent triangles.

D. A square is always a parallelogram.

Lesson 5-3: Equations and Formulas

Learn About It

You can describe a situation using an *equation*. An **equation** is a mathematical sentence with an equal sign.

Example 1

Nine more than three times a secret agent's code is equal to ninety-nine. Write an equation to describe this situation.

Let c = agent's code number	**Choose a variable.**
$3c$	**Write three times the code using the variable.**
$9 + 3c$	**Write the variable expression.**
$9 + 3c = 99$	**Write the equation.**

You can state a general rule or principle using a *formula*. A **formula** is an equation that shows the relationship between two or more variables.

Example 2

A taxicab company charges a flat fee of $2 plus an additional $.90 per mile. Write a formula to find the total cost, C, for each fare.

Let m = miles traveled	**Choose a variable.**
$.90 \times m$ or $.90m$	**Write a variable expression for the cost for miles driven.**
flat fee + cost for miles driven = total cost	**Describe the situation in words.**
$2 + .90m = C$	**Substitute values.**

1. Suppose a taxicab company charges a flat fee of $1.50 plus an additional $.75 per mile.

   a. Write a formula to find the total cost, C, for each fare.

   $\underline{C = 1.5 + .75m}$

   b. What is the fare for traveling 6 mi? $\underline{\$6.00}$

   c. What is the fare for traveling 7 mi? $\underline{\$6.75}$

   d. By what amount does the total cost of the fare increase for each additional mile driven?

   $\underline{\$.75}$

An **inequality** is a statement that compares two expressions using one of the following inequality symbols.

Inequality Symbol	Meaning
$>$	is greater than
$<$	is less than
$\geq$	is greater than or equal to
$\leq$	is less than or equal to

2. Write an inequality for each sentence.

   a. Twenty-three is greater than nine. <u>$23 > 9$</u>

   b. The number of students, s, is less than 20. <u>$s < 20$</u>

   c. The total, t, is greater than or equal to 55. <u>$t \geq 55$</u>

   d. A number, n, is not positive. <u>$n \leq 0$</u>

   e. The hourly wage, w, must not be less than \$6.50. <u>$w \geq 6.50$</u>

You can use inequalities to describe a situation.

Example 3

Nicholas made a purchase at the general store with a \$5 bill. He received change in nickels and dimes. Write an inequality to represent the change Nicholas received.

n	**Choose a variable for the number of nickels.**
$.05n$	**Write an expression for the value of the nickels.**
d	**Choose a variable for the number of dimes.**
$.10d$	**Write an expression for the value of the dimes.**
$.05n + .10d$	**Write an expression for the value of the change.**
$.05n + .10d < 5$	**Since the change must be less than \$5, use $<$.**

3. Is it possible Nicholas received 3 nickels and 2 dimes? Explain.

   <u>**Answers may vary. Sample: yes; the change would total \$.35, which**</u>

   <u>**is less than \$5.**</u>

4. Is it possible Nicholas's purchase cost \$5.90? Explain.

   <u>**Answers may vary. Sample: no; he could receive two nickels or one**</u>

   <u>**dime for change, but he could not receive both nickels and dimes.**</u>

Apply What You've Learned

5. Jack works at a carnival operating a coin toss booth. Customers may toss nickels and dimes in order to win various prizes. At the end of the night Jack counts the coins tossed that day. He has 3,170 coins with a total value of $217.

   a. Complete the equation that Jack's boss would use to check Jack's totals for the number of coins tossed. Use n and d for variables.

   number of coins tossed = $n + d$

   b. Complete the equation that Jack's boss would use to check Jack's totals for the value of the coins tossed. Use n and d for variables.

   value of the coins tossed = $.05n + .10d$

   c. Is it possible that 2,020 nickels and 1,160 dimes were tossed? Why or why not?

   <u>Answers may vary. Sample: no; this does not total 3,170 coins.</u>

   _____

   _____

6. **Circle A, B, C, or D.** Which of the following formulas correctly represents the perimeter of the rectangle pictured?

   I. $p = x + y + x + y$

   II. $p = 2x + 2y$

   III. $p = xy$

   IV. $p = 4xy$

   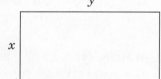

   A. I only

   B. III only

   C. I and II only

   D. II and IV only

7. **Circle A, B, C, or D.** John has a 10-question quiz. His father agrees to give him his regular $5 allowance plus 75 cents for each question he answers correctly on the quiz. However, he will not give John any more than twice his weekly allowance. Which inequality below accurately represents the situation described above?

   A. $0.75n \le 10$ **B.** $5 - 0.75 \le 10$

   C. $0.75n + 5 \le 10$ **D.** $(0.75 + 5)n \le 10$

8. Eva has $16 in her savings account. She earns $4.50 per hour babysitting. Eva wants to purchase a sweater for $55. Write an inequality that would be helpful to determine the least number of hours Eva must babysit in order to buy the sweater.

$16 + 4.50h \geq 55$

9. A car rental agency charges $27.95 per day plus $0.14 per mile.

a. Write a formula to find the total cost, C, of the car rental.

$C = 27.95d + .14m$

b. Suppose a car is rented for two days and is driven 150 mi. What is the total cost of the car rental?

$76.90

10. Circle A, B, C, or D.   An electrician charges $40 for each hour worked plus an additional $35 service charge. If C represents the electrician's total charges in dollars and h represents the number of hours worked, which formula below could be used to calculate C?

A. $C = 40 + 35 + h$

B. $C = 40 + 35h$

C. $C = (40)(35) + h$

D. $C = 40h + 35$

Integrated Review

Circle A, B, C, or D.

11. When purchasing an item, Nick gave a sales clerk a 20-dollar bill. The clerk gave him the item and change consisting of d one-dollar bills, q quarters, and n nickels. Which of the following expressions represents the cost in dollars of the item?

A. $20 - (d + q + n)$

B. $20 - d - .25q - .05n$

C. $d + q + n$

D. $100d + 25q + 5n$

12. In which quadrant does $P(x, y)$ lie if x is negative and y is negative?

A. I

B. II

C. III

D. IV

13. Which of these is one way to find $\frac{5}{8}$ of a number?

A. Multiply the number by $\frac{8}{5}$.

B. Divide the number by 5 and divide the result by 8.

C. Divide the number by 5 and multiply the result by 8.

D. Divide the number by 8 and multiply the result by 5.

Lesson 5-4: Percents

Learn About It

A percent is a comparison of a number to a set of 100. In the grid the amount shaded compared to the whole is 20 out of 100. You can write this as a fraction or a percent.

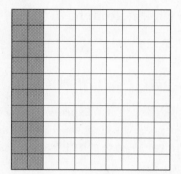

$$\frac{20}{100} \text{ or } 20\%$$

1. Write the shaded amount as a decimal. __0.2__

2. Suppose 73 out of 100 regions are shaded. Express the shaded amount as a fraction, percent, and decimal.
$\frac{73}{100}$, **73%, 0.73**

3. How would you represent $\frac{120}{100}$ using a grid? Express this amount as a percent and a decimal.

__Sample: use 2 grids, shading all of one and 2 columns__

__of the other; 120%; 1.2.__

You can solve a percent problem by translating the words of the problem into an equation. Recall what the following words and phrases mean.

Word or Phrase	Math Symbol
what, what percent	$x, \frac{x}{100}$
is	$=$
of	$\times$

There are three basic forms of percent problems. You can generate an equation to model each of them. The first type of percent problem requires you to find the percent of a number.

Example 1

What is 40% of 236?

$x = \frac{40}{100} \times 236$ **Generate an equation to model the problem.**

$x = 0.40 \times 236$ **Express the fraction as a decimal.**

$x = 94.4$ **Multiply.**

So, 94.4 is 40% of 236.

The second type of percent problem asks you to determine the percent one number is of another.

Example 2

42 is what percent of 75?

$42 = \frac{x}{100} \times 75$ **Translate into an equation.**

$42 = \frac{75x}{100}$ **Simplify.**

$42 = 0.75x$ **Express the fraction as a decimal.**

$56 = x$ **Divide.**

So, 42 is 56% of 75.

An example of the third type of percent problem is given below.

Example 3

11 is 55% of what number?

$11 = \frac{55}{100} \times x$ **Translate into an equation.**

$11 = 0.55x$ **Express the fraction as a decimal.**

$\frac{11}{0.55} = \frac{0.55x}{0.55}$ **Divide each side by 0.55.**

$20 = x$ **Divide.**

So, 11 is 55% of 20.

You can use these three forms of percent problems to solve more difficult word problems.

3. In the United States, about 46% of the population wears glasses or contact lenses. How many people would you expect to wear glasses or contact lenses in a group of 300 people? Decide which statement represents the problem and solve.

300 is 46% of what number?
What is 46% of 300?
46 is what percent of 300?

<u>the second statement; 138 people</u>

4. Graphing calculator sales totaled $1,500 during the second week of school. Sales for the first week were higher. In fact, $1,500 was only 40% of the first week sales. How much were the total sales during the first week of school? Decide which statement represents the problem and solve.

1,500 is 40% of what number?
What is 40% of 1,500?
40 is what percent of 1,500?

<u>the first statement; $3750</u>

Translate each sentence into an equation. Then solve.

5. 48 is what percent of 150? $\underline{\quad 48 = \frac{x}{100} \cdot 150; 32\% \quad}$

6. What is 60% of 174? $\underline{\quad x = 0.60 \cdot 174; 104.4 \quad}$

7. 14 is 80% of what number? $\underline{\quad 14 = 0.80x; 17.5 \quad}$

8. 88 is what percent of 250? $\underline{\quad 88 = \frac{x}{100} \cdot 250; 35.2\% \quad}$

9. 50 is 40% of what number? $\underline{\quad 50 = \frac{40}{100} \cdot x; 125 \quad}$

10. What is 250% of 80? $\underline{\quad x = \frac{250}{100} \cdot 80; 200 \quad}$

11. What is 37% of 140? $\underline{\quad x = 0.37 \cdot 140; 51.8 \quad}$

12. 42 is 15% of what number? $\underline{\quad 42 = \frac{15}{100} \cdot x; 280 \quad}$

13. There are 50 apartments in Sara's building. Sara delivers the morning paper to 15 of these apartments. To what percent of the apartments does Sara deliver the paper each morning? Decide which statement represents the problem and solve.

50 is 15% of what number?
What is 15% of 50?
15 is what percent of 50?

<u>the third statement; 30%</u>

Sara receives a $.75 tip for each apartment to which she delivers the morning paper. How much does she earn in tips each week?

<u>$11.25</u>

14. Circle A, B, C, or D. The number of Central High students who gave to the United Fund this year was 342. This figure is 110% of what it was the previous year. This means that

A. 10 more Central High School students gave to the United Fund.

B. the number of Central High School students giving to the United Fund decreased from last year to this year.

C. the number of Central High School students giving money to the United Fund this year did not change from last year.

D. the number of Central High School students giving to the United Fund increased from last year to this year.

15. Rashid is the president of the sophomore class and needs to present the results of their candy sales at the next meeting. The class sold 5,400 boxes of plain candy and 2,800 boxes of peanut candy.

a. What is the total number of boxes of candy sold? 8,200 boxes

b. What percent of the total number of boxes of candy sold were plain candy? Round to the nearest whole number.

66%

c. What percent of the total number of boxes of candy sold were peanut candy? Round to the nearest whole number.

34%

d. Sketch a circle graph that Rashid might use to present the results at the sophomore class meeting.

Sophomore Class Candy Sale

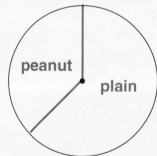

peanut   plain

16. A school spends $1\frac{1}{2}$% of its budget on supplies. If the supply budget is $75,000, what is the total school budget? Write the statement that represents the problem and solve.

75,000 is $1\frac{1}{2}$% of what number?

75,000 = 0.015x; $5,000,000

17. Circle A, B, C, or D. In which set are all three values equal?

A. 42%, 0.042, $\frac{42}{100}$

B. 0.42%, 0.42, $\frac{42}{100}$

C. 42%, 0.42, $\frac{42}{100}$ *(circled)*

D. 0.42%, 0.0042, $\frac{42}{100}$

18. Circle A, B, C, or D. Clarkson's chain of mini-marts reported sales for the month at $14.6 million. That figure was 41% of the previous month's sales. Approximately how much were Clarkson's mini-marts' sales for the previous month?

A. $3,560,000

B. $35,600,000 *(circled)*

C. $356,000,000

D. $356,000

Integrated Review

Circle A, B, C, or D.

19. Danny participated in a swimathon to raise money for the local food pantry. His neighbor, Mrs. Kerrigan, sponsored him for $.15 per lap. Danny asked Mrs. Kerrigan for $3.60. Choose the equation that Mrs. Kerrigan could solve to determine how many laps Danny completed.

A. $0.15(3.60) = l$

B. $0.15 \div l = 3.60$

C. $0.15l = 3.60$ *(circled)*

D. $0.15 = 3.60l$

20. It cost a store $40.80 to purchase and assemble a computer software package. If the store is to make a 15 percent profit on the sale of each package, which of the following computations will give the number of dollars the store should charge for each package?

A. $40.80 + 0.15$

B. $(0.15)(40.80)$

C. $(0.15)(40.80) + (0.15)$

D. $40.80 + (0.15)(40.80)$ *(circled)*

21. Oprah's teacher allows students to decide whether to use mean, median, or mode as their test average. Oprah will receive the highest average if she uses the mean. Which set of test grades are Oprah's?

A. 74, 80, 92, 82, 92 *(circled)*

B. 74, 80, 74, 82, 85

C. 74, 80, 92, 85, 74

D. 74, 80, 70, 71, 80

Lesson 5-5: More Percents

Learn About It

You can use what you know about percents to determine the discount price of an item.

1. A new CD player regularly priced at $270 is on sale at 25% off of that price. What is the sale price of the CD player?

   a. Write the equation that represents the amount of discount.

   $x = 0.25 \cdot 270$

   b. Solve the equation. The solution tells you how much money will be *deducted* from the regular price of the CD player.

   $67.50

   c. What is the sale price of the CD player? $202.50

   d. Could you use the statement *What is 75% of 270?* to find the sale price of the CD player? Explain.

   Answers may vary. Sample: yes; taking away 25% of a number leaves you with 75% of that number.

Remember to be extra cautious when working with percents. The following problem is an example of a common error that can be made.

2. Hana's store is having a sale on jeans and cuts the original price by 40%.

   a. The original price of a pair of jeans is $36. What is the sale price?

   $21.60

   After the sale Hana tells her helper to raise the price of the jeans by 40% of the sale price. Her helper puts the jeans back to their original price.

   b. Explain how you would know if the helper priced the jeans correctly.

   Answers may vary. Sample: no; 40% of the sale price is less than 40% of the original price, so the new price should be less than the original price.

   c. At what price should the helper mark the jeans?

   $30.24

Apply What You've Learned

3. Identical sweaters are on sale in two different stores. In the first store, the sweater is on sale at 70% of the original price of $45. In the second store, the sweater is on sale at 60% of the original price of $48.

   a. What is the sale price of the sweater at the first store?

   $31.50

   b. What is the sale price of the sweater at the second store?

   $28.80

   c. Which store offers the better buy? the second store

4. Six friends are planning to eat at a restaurant where complete dinners range in price from $8.00 to $15.00 per person. They want to leave the waiter a tip amounting to 15% of their total bill.

   a. What is the least amount the six friends will need to leave for their combined total tip?

   $7.20

   b. What is the greatest amount the six friends will need to leave for their combined total tip?

   $13.50

   c. Suppose two people order dinners costing $12.50 and the other four order dinners costing $9.75. What is the group's combined total tip?

   $9.60

5. A picture with dimensions 8 in. by 10 in. is placed on a copy machine which is set to reduce all dimensions by 35%.

   a. What will the dimensions of the picture be after it is reduced?

   5.2 in. by 6.5 in.

   b. Will the new picture fit in a frame with dimensions 5 in. by 7 in.? Why or why not?

   Answers may vary. Sample: no; both dimensions are greater than

   5 in.

6. Of the 525 people responding to a public opinion poll, 244 answered *Yes* when asked if they liked their school mascot and 176 answered *No*. The remainder of the respondents were undecided.

   a. How many of the respondents were undecided? 105

   b. What percent of the respondents were undecided? 20%

7. Circle A, B, C, or D. For a sale, a shopkeeper lowers the price of an item by 20 percent. After the sale, the shopkeeper raises the price of that item by 20 percent. The price of the item now is

A. more than the original price.

B. less than the original price.

C. the same as the original price.

D. There is not enough information to compare the two prices.

8. Circle A, B, C, or D. A new bicycle regularly priced at $224 is on sale at 30% off of that price. What is the sale price of the bicycle?

A. $67.20   **B.** $156.80   **C.** $194.00   **D.** $217.28

9. Circle A, B, C, or D. This year the number of seniors taking mathematics is 5 percent greater than it was last year. If there were 40 seniors taking mathematics last year, how many seniors are taking mathematics this year?

A. 42   **B.** 45   **C.** 48   **D.** 60

Integrated Review

Circle A, B, C, or D.

10. Which of the following is NOT a way to find 125% of a number?

A. Multiply the number by 1.25.

B. Divide the number by 4 and add the result to the number.

C. Divide the number by 4 and multiply the result by 5.

D. Multiply the number by .25 and multiply the result by 4.

11. The table at the right indicates a relationship between a and b. Which of the equations expresses the relationship between a and b that is indicated in the table?

A. $b = -a^2$

B. $b = a - 2$

C. $b = 2a - 3$

D. $b = a + 2$

a	b
0	−3
1	−1
2	1
. . .	. . .
5	7
. . .	. . .
8	13

Lesson 5-6: Solving Equations

Work Together

Work in your groups to explore equations. An equation is like a scale. The weights on both sides of a scale must be the same for the scale to balance. For an equation to be true, the values on both sides of the equation must be equivalent.

1. Each cylinder weighs 5 lb. The weight of each cube is not known.

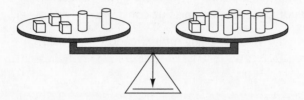

   a. How would you remove matching weights from each side so that cylinders are found only on the right side of the scale?

     <u>**Remove 2 cylinders from each side.**</u>

   b. Complete the diagram to show the remaining weights.

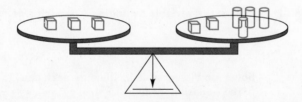

   c. Using the diagram you drew in part (b), how would you remove matching weights from each side so that cubes are found only on the left side of the scale?

     <u>**Remove 2 cubes from each side.**</u>

   d. Complete the diagram to show the remaining weights.

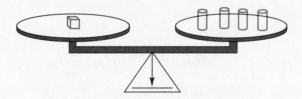

   e. How many times heavier is the cube than the cylinder? Explain.

     <u>**Answers may vary. Sample: the cube is 4 times heavier than the**</u>

     <u>**cylinder because one cube is in balance with 4 cylinders.**</u>

   f. What is the weight of a cube? <u>**20 lb**</u>

You can solve an equation using algebra by following the steps that are listed in the chart below.

> **Solving Equations**
>
> 1. Remove parentheses using the distributive property.
>
> 2. Simplify each side of the equation.
>
> 3. Use addition or subtraction to isolate the variable on one side of the equation and put constants on the other.
>
> 4. Solve for the variable using multiplication or division.

The following example shows how to solve a two-step equation.

Example 1

Solve $2x - 3 = 10$.

$$2x - 3 = 10$$

$$2x - 3 + 3 = 10 + 3 \qquad \text{Isolate the variable by adding 3 to each side.}$$

$$2x = 13$$

$$\frac{2x}{2} = \frac{13}{2} \qquad \text{Solve for the variable by dividing each side of the equation by 2.}$$

$$x = 7.5$$

You will have to use the distributive property to solve some equations.

Example 2

Solve $-3(x + 6) = 21$.

$$-3(x + 6) = 21$$

$$-3x - 18 = 21 \qquad \text{Use the distributive property.}$$

$$-3x - 18 + 18 = 21 + 18 \qquad \text{Add 18 to each side.}$$

$$-3x = 39$$

$$\frac{-3x}{-3} = \frac{39}{-3} \qquad \text{Divide each side by } -3.$$

$$x = -13$$

Some equations contain variables on both sides.

Example 3

Solve $7x - 9 = 4x + 15$.

$$7x - 9 = 4x + 15$$

$$7x - 9 - 4x = 4x + 15 - 4x \qquad \textbf{Subtract 4x from each side.}$$

$$3x - 9 = 15$$

$$3x - 9 + 9 = 15 + 9 \qquad \textbf{Add 9 to each side.}$$

$$3x = 24$$

$$\frac{3x}{3} = \frac{24}{3} \qquad \textbf{Divide each side by 3.}$$

$$x = 8$$

You can use an equation to solve a word problem.

Example 4

The lengths of the sides of a triangle are in the ratio 3:4:5. The perimeter of the triangle is 84 cm. Find the length of each side.

You can express the sides of the triangle as a multiple of the ratio $3:4:5$. Let the lengths of the sides be $3x$, $4x$, and $5x$.

$$3x + 4x + 5x = 84 \qquad \textbf{Write an equation.}$$

$$12x = 84 \qquad \textbf{Simplify.}$$

$$\frac{12x}{12} = \frac{84}{12} \qquad \textbf{Divide each side by 12.}$$

$$x = 7$$

So, the lengths of the sides of the triangle are 21 cm, 28 cm, and 35 cm.

2. The measures of the angles of a triangle are in the ratio 1:1:2.

a. Represent the measures of the angles using variable x.

$\underline{x, x, 2x}$

b. Write an equation to represent this situation. (*Hint*: The sum of the measures of the angles of a triangle is 180°.)

$\underline{x + x + 2x = 180}$

c. What is the measure of each angle? $\underline{45°, 45°, 90°}$

Solve each equation.

3. $2x + 3 = 10$ _3.5 or $3\frac{1}{2}$_

4. $\frac{2}{3}x + 4 = 6$ _3_

5. $\frac{3}{4}x - 6 = 18$ _32_

6. $-3(x - 6) = 21$ _-1_

7. $-14 = -3(x - 4)$ _$8\frac{2}{3}$_

8. $8x - 7 = -5 - 3x$ _$\frac{2}{11}$_

9. $4x + 8 = 14 - 4x$ _$\frac{3}{4}$_

10. $7x - \sqrt{64} = 17x - 3$ _-0.5_

11. $9 - (x - 2) = 4x + 6$ _1_

12. $12x - (3x + 1) = 2x - 5$ _$-\frac{4}{7}$_

13. Circle A, B, C, or D. Which sequence of steps will not solve the equation $\frac{1}{3}x + 9 = 12$?

(A) Subtract 9 from both sides, then divide both sides by 3.

B. Subtract 9 from both sides, then multiply both sides by 3.

C. Multiply both sides by 3, then subtract 27 from both sides.

D. Divide both sides by $\frac{1}{3}$, then subtract 27 from both sides.

14. There are three times as many girls as boys at a birthday party. There are 36 people at the party.

a. Let b represent the number of boys at the birthday party. Write a variable expression for the number of girls at the party.

_3b_

b. Write an equation to represent the situation.

_$b + 3b = 36$_

c. Solve for variable b. What does this number represent?

9; this is the number of boys at the party.

d. How many girls are at the birthday party? _27 girls_

15. The perimeter of a rectangle is 185 ft. The ratio of the length to the width is 2:3. What are the dimensions of the rectangle?

_37 ft by 55.5 ft_

16. Each cube weighs 2 lb. The weight of a pyramid is not known.

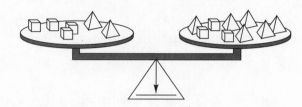

a. Is a cube or a pyramid heavier? Explain. _____

A cube is heavier, because one cube balances with 4 pyramids.

b. What is the weight of a pyramid? $\frac{1}{2}$ lb _____

17. Circle A, B, C, or D. The general partners in a small company, Miranda, Cohen, and Brown, share its profits in the ratio of 3:2:5, respectively. If that company's profits amount to $24,300 this year, what is Mr. Miranda's share?

A. $2,430   **B.** $7,290   **C.** $8,100   **D.** $14,580

Integrated Review

Circle A, B, C, or D.

1. Four friends are planning to eat at a restaurant where complete dinners cost between $12.00 and $17.00 per person. They want to leave the waiter a tip amounting to 15% of their total bill. Which of the following is the closest to what the four friends will need to leave for their combined *total* tip?

A. $2.00   **B.** $4.00   **C.** $9.00   **D.** $15.00

2. The diameter of a dime is around

A. 200 mm   **B.** 20 cm   **C.** 2 m   **D.** 2 cm

3. Which statements below are equivalent to one another?

  I. In a year, Terry spends $400 on a health-club membership and $1,600 on cookies.

  II. In a year, Terry spends 4 times as much on cookies as he does on his health-club membership.

  III. In a year, Terry spends 20% as much on his health-club membership as he does on cookies.

A. I and II only   **B.** I and III only

C. II and III only   **D.** I, II, and III

Lesson 5-7: Linear Equations

Learn About It

Some equations contain two variables. An ordered pair that makes an equation in two variables true is a **solution** of the equation.

Example 1

Tell whether the ordered pair $(2, -1)$ is a solution of the equation $y = -2x + 3$.

$y = -2x + 3$

$-1 = -2(2) + 3$ **Substitute the first number of the ordered pair for x and the second number for y.**

$-1 = -4 + 3$

$-1 = -1$ ✔

True, so the ordered pair $(2, -1)$ is a solution.

---

1. Tell whether each ordered pair is a solution of the equation $y = 5x - 4$.

    a. $(2, 6)$ <u>yes</u>   **b.** $(-1, 9)$ <u>no</u>

You can find solutions for an equation with two variables by using a table of values.

Example 2

Find three ordered pairs that satisfy the equation $y = -x + 3$.

First, choose three values for x. Let's use $-2, 0,$ and 3.

Then, use a table of values like the one below to organize your data. Substitute x values into the equation to find y values.

x	$y = -x + 3$	y	(x, y)
-2	$y = -(-2) + 3 = 5$	5	$(-2, 5)$
0	$y = -(0) + 3 = 3$	3	$(0, 3)$
3	$y = -(3) + 3 = 0$	0	$(3, 0)$

The ordered pairs $(-2, 5), (0, 3),$ and $(3, 0)$ are solutions of the equation $y = -x + 3$.

You can use a graph to show the solutions of an equation.

2. Graph the equation $y = 2x - 1$.

a. Complete the table of values below to find three solutions of the equation $y = 2x - 1$.

x	y = 2x − 1	y	(x, y)
−1	y = 2(−1) − 1	−3	(−1, −3)
0	y = 2(0) − 1	−1	(0, −1)
3	y = 2(3) − 1	5	(3, 5)

b. Graph these ordered pairs on the coordinate plane below. Connect these points with a line.

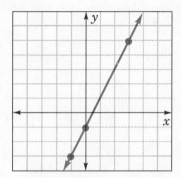

c. Each ordered pair on the graph is a solution of the linear equation $y = 2x - 1$. How can you tell by the graph that (2, 3) is a solution of this equation?

<u>The graph of (2, 3) lies on the line.</u>

Apply What You've Learned

Determine whether each point lies on the graph of $y = \frac{4}{3}x - 2$.

3. (3, 2) <u>yes</u>

4. (−3, 6) <u>no</u>

5. (0, 2) <u>no</u>

6. (9, 10) <u>yes</u>

7. Circle A, B, C, or D. Which of the following points lies on the graph of $2x - y = 4$?

A. (−2, 8)   **B.** (1, −2)   **C.** (2, −8)   **D.** (−1, 6)

8. Complete the table of values to find three points that satisfy the equation $y = -\frac{1}{2}x + 3$.

x	$y = -\frac{1}{2}x + 3$	y	(x, y)
−4	$y = -\frac{1}{2}(-4) + 3$	5	(−4, 5)
2	$y = -\frac{1}{2}(2) + 3$	2	(2, 2)
8	$y = -\frac{1}{2}(8) + 3$	−1	(8, −1)

9. Circle A, B, C, or D. Which of the following equations represents the line containing the points given in the diagram below?

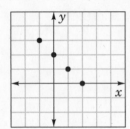

   A. $y = x + 3$

   B. $y = x - 3$

   C. $y = -x$

   (D.) $y = 2 - x$

10. The equation $y = x$ is graphed on the coordinate plane below. Points A, B, and C lie on this line.

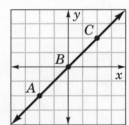

   a. What are the coordinates of points A, B, and C?

   (−2, −2), (0, 0), (2, 2)

   b. Put your pencil on point A. Slide your pencil two units down and plot a point D. What are the coordinates of point D?

   (−2, −4)

   c. Put your pencil on point B. Slide your pencil two units down and plot a point E. What are the coordinates of point E?

   (0, −2)

   d. Put your pencil on point C. Slide your pencil two units down and plot a point F. What are the coordinates of point F?

   (2, 0)

   e. Connect points D, E, and F. This line is a translation, or slide, of the graph of the equation $y = x$. What is the equation of the new line?

   $y = x - 2$

11. Circle A, B, C, or D. The graph of $y = 2x - 3$ is shown. Which statement is true about the graph of $y = 2x - 1$?

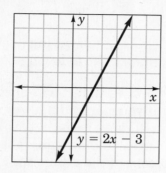

A. It intersects the graph of $y = 2x - 3$.

B. It is a translation of the graph $y = 2x - 3$ two units to the right.

C. It is perpendicular to the x-axis.

D. It is a translation of the graph $y = 2x - 3$ two units up.

Integrated Review

Circle A, B, C, or D.

12. What is the weight of one of the cubes if each pyramid weighs 2 pounds?

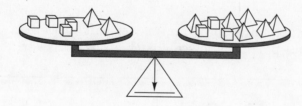

A. $\frac{1}{4}$ pound

B. 4 pounds

C. 6 pounds

D. 8 pounds

13. Which of these sequences of steps transforms the equation $\frac{1}{2}x + 6 = 14$ into the equation $x = 16$?

A. Subtract 6 from both sides and multiply both sides by 2.

B. Multiply both sides by 2 and subtract 6 from both sides.

C. Multiply both sides by $\frac{1}{2}$ and add 6 to both sides.

D. Subtract 6 from both sides and divide both sides by 2.

Lesson 5-8: Answering Open-Ended Questions

Work Together

Work with a partner to improve your skills at answering open-ended questions. First work individually to answer the following question.

1. The Warlock Electronics Store advertises that it will never be undersold. The Warlock says that if you can find a lower regularly advertised price from another store for any item that Warlock sells, the Warlock will match that lower price and also give you an additional reduction that is 10 percent of the difference in the prices. Is the additional reduction significant? Present a convincing argument to support your answer; include a simple example as part of your argument.   Answers may vary. Check students' work.

2. The scoring guide below explains how your answer will be scored. Exchange work with your partner and score each other's answer.

Scoring Guide

3   A statement that additional reduction is not significant with explanation acknowledging that 10% of a <u>difference</u> is not that great; or reduction <u>is</u> significant with reasonable argument and example; or reduction <u>may be</u> significant with reasonable argument and examples showing both. A specific appropriate example must be given and worked out.

2   A focus on 10% of a difference but argument not convincing, or example not appropriate or lacking, or indication of significant/not significant missing.

1   A focus on 10% of a price, not 10% of a difference in prices, with statement of significance of reduction and example.

0   A focus on 10% of price and indication of not significant and/or no example or blank or irrelevant of other incorrect response.

© Prentice-Hall, Inc.

Learn About It

Sample responses to this open-ended question are shown below.

Sample 1

> The reduction depends on the amount the item
> costs. If the item costs $1,000. Then it would be
> reduced $100. But if the item cost $50 it
> would be reduced only $5. That 10% would only
> really cover the taxes you pay on the product.

3. This response scored a 1. Why do you think this response received this score?

<u>Answers may vary. Sample: the response focuses on 10% of a price,</u>

<u>rather than 10% of the difference in prices.</u>

_____

_____

Sample 2

> If the Warlock's prices are as close to bottom
> as they say, then this discount is not significant
> at all. If you have a $75.00 walkman at store X
> and it costs $76.00 at Warlock's the additional
> discount would be exactly 1¢. Your total cost
> would be $74.99 at Warlock's. Not a huge
> difference from $75.00.

4. This response scored a 2. Why do you think this response received this score?

<u>Answers may vary. Sample: the 10% discount of the difference is the</u>

<u>focus, but the example has mathematical errors.</u>

_____

_____

5. Look back at your answer to Question 1. If you did not score a 3, use what you've learned to write an improved answer.
Check students' work

Apply What You've Learned

6. A restaurant is advertising two types of discount coupons. The BUY ONE, GET ONE FREE type of coupon is good for exactly one free meal when another meal of equal or greater value is purchased. The SAVE $5 type of coupon is good for a $5 discount on every meal. You and a friend decide to have dinner at the restaurant. You order a dinner priced at $12.95. Your friend is having a difficult time choosing between a dinner priced at $13.95 and another priced at $8.95. Will your friend's choice of dinner affect the coupons you will use to get the "better" deal? Present a convincing argument to support your answer.

SCORING GUIDE:

3   Correctly analyzes price options and presents a convincing argument concluding that BUY ONE, GET ONE FREE is better when friend's meal is more than $10.

2   Gives correct answers but argument contains minor computational errors OR presents clear argument but incorrectly concludes that BUY ONE, GET ONE FREE is always better.

1   incompletely analyzes price options OR gives correct answer with no explanation OR incorrect answer with reasonable argument.

0   inappropriate answer or no answer.

7. Elena commutes from her home in Dunellen to Jersey City State College. She takes the express train from Dunellen to Newark, takes the Path from Newark to Journal Square Jersey City and then takes a bus from Journal Square to the College. It is 30 miles from Dunellen to Newark, 10 miles from Newark to Jersey City by Path and 8 miles from Journal Square to the College. The train averages 60 mph, the Path averages 50 mph and the bus averages 30 mph. If Elena has an 8 o'clock class, what time should Elena leave home?

SCORING GUIDE:

3   correct calculation of time taken on each form of transportation (train – 30 min, Path – 12 min, bus – 16 min), and correct subtraction to find that the latest time she should leave is 7:02, if walking and waiting time is disregarded.

2   incorrect leaving time due to minor computational errors in transportation time OR incorrect subtraction from 8:00.

1   correct leaving time with no work shown OR computational errors in transportation time and leaving time.

0   inappropriate answer or no answer.

8. A supermarket lowered the original price of an item by 20%. After the sale the manager told the clerk to raise the price of the item by 20% of its sale price. The clerk marked the item with the original price. Was the clerk right or wrong in doing that? Present a convincing argument to support your answer. You may wish to include a simple, specific example as part of your argument.

SCORING GUIDE:

3   Presents a convincing argument why the clerk was wrong.

2   Presents a convincing argument why the clerk was wrong with minor computational errors.

1   Decides clerk was wrong with weak or incomplete argument OR presents a clear argument with wrong answer.

0   inappropriate answer or no answer.

Circle A, B, C, or D.

1. One leg of a right triangle is twice as long as the other leg. If the length of the shorter leg is x, which of the expressions below represents the area of that triangle?

   (A.) x^2 **B.** $2x^2$ **C.** $2x$ **D.** $\frac{1}{2}x$

2. If $x = 3$, which of the following does NOT equal 9?

   A. x^2 **B.** $(-x)^2$

   C. $(-x)(-x)$ **(D.)** $-x^2$

3. In a candy factory, 4 pieces of candy out of every n pieces tested are rejected, on the average. What fraction of those n pieces is <u>not</u> rejected? (*Hint*: substitute values for n.)

   A. $\frac{n}{4}$ **B.** $\frac{4}{n}$ **C.** $\frac{n-4}{4}$ **(D.)** $\frac{n-4}{n}$

4. Suppose that each time a ball bounces, it goes up $\frac{1}{2}$ the distance it fell. If that ball is dropped from a height of x feet, which of these expressions represents the total distance it has traveled when it hits the floor for the fifth time?

   A. $x + \frac{1}{2} + \frac{1}{4} + \frac{1}{8} + \frac{1}{16}$

   B. $x + \frac{1}{2} + \frac{1}{2} + \frac{1}{4} + \frac{1}{4} + \frac{1}{8} + \frac{1}{8} + \frac{1}{16} + \frac{1}{16}$

   (C.) $x + \frac{x}{2} + \frac{x}{2} + \frac{x}{4} + \frac{x}{4} + \frac{x}{8} + \frac{x}{8} + \frac{x}{16} + \frac{x}{16}$

   D. $(x)\left(\frac{1}{2}\right)\left(\frac{1}{4}\right)\left(\frac{1}{8}\right)\left(\frac{1}{16}\right)$

5. The formula for changing temperature from Celsius to Fahrenheit is $F = \frac{9}{5}C + 32$. If the temperature of something is $60°$ C, what is its temperature in degrees Fahrenheit?

   A. $18.4°$ F   **B.** $33.8°$ F   **(C.)** $140°$ F   **D.** $165.6°$ F

6. 18 is what percent of 120? <u>**15%**</u>

7. A house painter uses the following formula to determine how much to charge for doing a job. C is the total charge in dollars, and h is the number of hours of work required to complete the job.

$$C = 24h + 12$$

   This formula indicates that for every additional hour the house painter works, the total charge is increased by

   A. \$12   **(B.)** \$24   **C.** \$36   **D.** \$288

8. Which of these inequalities would be most helpful in solving the problem stated below?

Avi spent an afternoon playing pinball and eating small bags of popcorn. A pinball game cost $.50 and a bag of popcorn cost $.90. Avi had only $10 to spend. If he had 2 bags of popcorn and played as many pinball games as he could, how many games did he play?

A. $0.50x + 1.80 \leq 10$ **B.** $x + 1.80 \leq 10$

C. $0.90x + 1.50 \leq 10$ **D.** $3x + 0.50 \leq 10$

9. Mrs. Robinson purchases a new car for $8800 plus 6% sales tax. How much more would she have paid for the car if the sales tax were 7% instead of 6%?

A. $88   **B.** $198   **C.** $528   **D.** $616

10. A diagram of a rectangle with dimensions 6 inches by 8 inches is placed in a copy machine which is set to enlarge all dimensions by 10 percent. Will the resulting figure fit on an $8\frac{1}{2}$ by 11 sheet of paper?

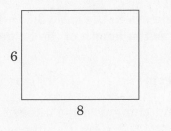 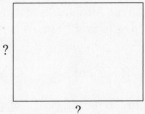

A. Yes, it will fit with room to spare.

B. Yes, it will just fit with no room to spare.

C. No, one dimension will fit, but not the other.

D. No, both dimensions will be too large.

11. Last week, Georgette earned $360. To estimate the amount of her paycheck after deductions, she first adds and then rounds to the nearest percent the deductions indicated below:

Federal Income Tax:	15.0%
FICA (Social Security):	7.5%
Unemployment Insurance:	.25%
State Income Tax:	2.5%

Her estimate of the amount of her paycheck is between

A. $350 and $400.   **B.** $300 and $350.

C. $250 and $300.   **D.** $50 and $100.

12. Which sequence of steps will NOT solve the equation $\frac{1}{2}x + 4 = 10$ for x?

  A. Subtract 4 from both sides, then multiply both sides by 2.

  (B.) Multiply both sides by 2, then subtract 4 from both sides.

  C. Divide both sides by $\frac{1}{2}$, then subtract 8 from both sides.

  D. Subtract 4 from both sides, then divide both sides by $\frac{1}{2}$.

13. If $3y - 5 = 2 + 14y$, then $y =$

  (A.) $-\frac{7}{11}$ **B.** $-\frac{3}{17}$ **C.** $\frac{3}{17}$ **D.** $\frac{7}{11}$

14. Sally is running a game booth at the school fair. She carefully collects exactly 30 cents from every player. At the end of the fair, she must count the money collected. She counts it four times, getting a different total each time. Which of the following could be the correct total?

  A. $22.45   **(B.)** $22.50   **C.** $22.60   **D.** $22.65

15. The lengths of the three sides of a triangle are in the ratio 3:5:6. The perimeter of the triangle is 42 cm. What is the length of the longest side of the triangle?

  A. 15 cm   **(B.)** 18 cm   **C.** 9 cm   **D.** 42 cm

16. Consider the number 36; some pairs of matching positive integer factors are (2, 18), (3, 12), (4, 9), (6, 6), . . . (12, 3), (18, 2). Suppose someone graphs all possible pairs of matching positive integer factors of a given positive integer. Which of the following most likely represents such a graph?

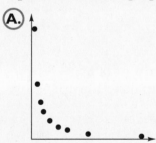

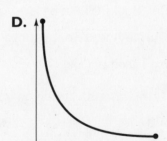

Write your answer in the boxes at the top of the grid, one number (or decimal point) per box. Then fill in the correct circle below each box.

17. Solve for S:

$$\frac{5}{6}S - \sqrt{36} = 3.75$$

1	1	.	7
/	/	/	/
.	.	●	.
0	0	0	0
●	●	1	1
2	2	2	2
3	3	3	3
4	4	4	4
5	5	5	5
6	6	6	6
7	7	7	●
8	8	8	8
9	9	9	9

Answer the following open-ended question in the space below.

18. On the grid below, sketch triangle ABC if the coordinates of point A are (2, 8), the coordinates of point B are (10, 8) and the coordinates of point C are (2, 2). What is the perimeter of the triangle? Explain in detail how you found the perimeter.

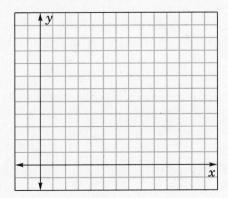

SCORING GUIDE:

3   Graphs triangle correctly and computes perimeter correctly (24). Explanation includes use of the distance formula to find $AD = 8$ and $AC = 6$ and either use of the Pythagorean theorem to find $BC = 10$ or recognition that it is a Pythagorean triple. Perimeter is then found by adding the lengths of the three sides.

2   Correct graph and perimeter but weak or incomplete explanation OR correct graph with incorrect perimeter due to computational errors with appropriate explanation.

1   Incorrect graph and/or perimeter with weak explanation.

0   inappropriate answer or no answer.

Alternative Assessment Project

Here are some projects that will demonstrate your understanding of the topics in this chapter.

Project 1

Write a word problem whose solution requires the solver to write a multi-step equation. Include a detailed solution and be able to explain your problem clearly.

SCORING GUIDE:

3   The student presents a clear problem requiring a multi-step equation and is able to explain its solution.

2   The student presents a clear problem requiring a multi-step equation but fails to explain its solution adequately OR presents a one-step equation with a clear solution.

1   The student presents a simple problem with an explanation.

0   The student answers inappropriately or fails to attempt an answer.

Project 2

Write a story that demonstrates understanding of the mathematical terms variable, expression, equality, inequality, and equation.

SCORING GUIDE:

3   The student writes a story using all the vocabulary terms correctly.

2   The student writes a story using four of the vocabulary terms correctly.

1   The student writes a story using only two of the vocabulary terms correctly.

0   The student answers inappropriately or fails to attempt an answer.

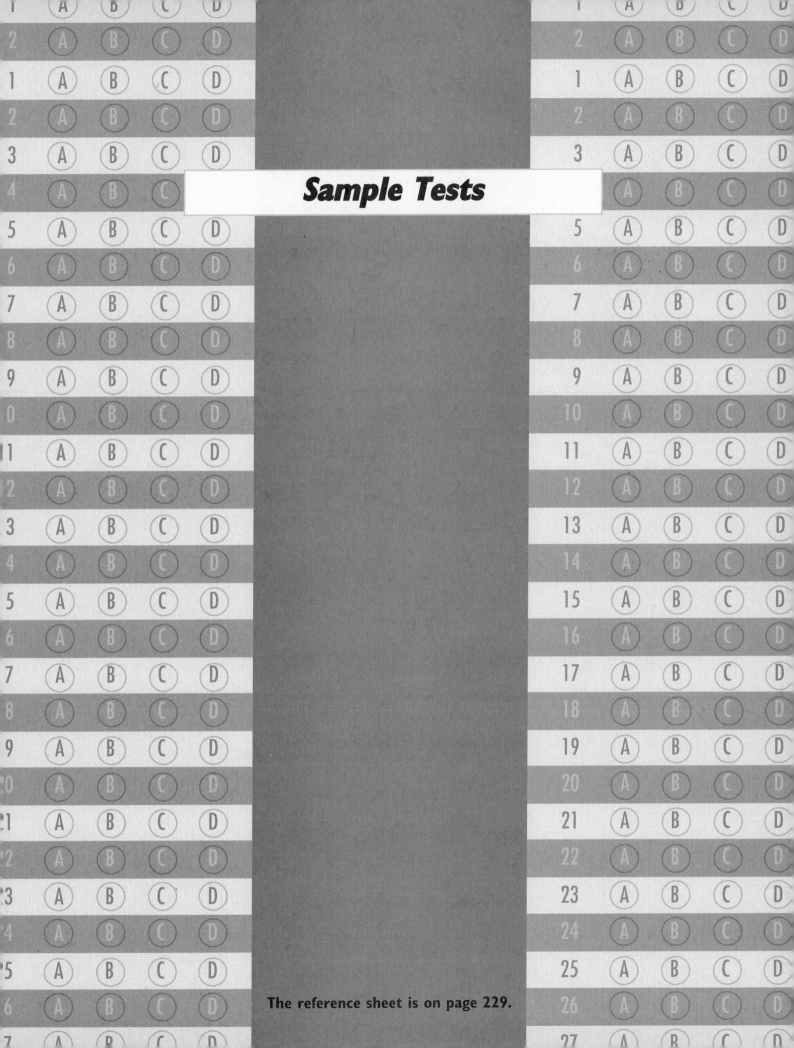

Sample Tests

The reference sheet is on page 229.

MATHEMATICS SECTION

DIRECTIONS FOR MATHEMATICS PART 1

You will have 35 minutes to work on Part 1. Work carefully and try to answer as many questions right as you can. Do not spend too much time on any one question. If you do not know an answer, make the best choice you can and go on to the next question.

You may use scratch paper or any space in the test booklet for working out your answers, but mark all of your answers on your answer folder. Mark only one answer for each question. If you make a mistake or wish to change an answer, be sure to erase your first choice completely.

You have received a Mathematics Reference Sheet which provides formulas and other useful information. Open-ended items on some forms of the test will require that you fold and tear along the perforations at the bottom of your reference sheet to make paper geometric shapes. You may use the information on the reference sheet to help solve problems on the test.

There are additional directions for the last two questions in Part 1. Follow these directions carefully when you mark your answers on the grids provided for questions 22 and 23. Work until you reach the end of Part 1. Please do not go on to Part 2 until you receive further directions. If you finish Part 1 before the time is up, you may go back and check your work.

MATHEMATICS PART 1

DIRECTIONS: Work all problems. Record your answer choices in the spaces provided for Mathematics Part 1 on your answer folder. Mark the letter for your answer in the appropriate space. UNLESS THE PROBLEM STATES OTHERWISE, DO NOT FIGURE SALES TAX IN YOUR ANSWERS TO PROBLEMS INVOLVING PURCHASES.

1. There are three times as many girls as boys at a party. If there are 36 people at the party, how many of them are boys?

   A. 9

   B. 12

   C. 15

   D. 27

2. Consider the following pattern in which the exponents are integers:

   $$2^3, 2^2, 2^1, ...$$

   If this pattern continues, what is the value of the seventh term in the pattern?

   A. $\frac{1}{2}$

   B. $\frac{1}{8}$

   C. -6

   D. -8

3. Joe ordered tables to be set up for the junior-senior prom; each of the available tables accommodated exactly 8 people. He knew that 251 people would come to the prom. He used his calculator to divide 251 by 8 and got 31.375. Therefore, he ordered 31 tables to be set up for the prom. His decision was

   A. good because he ordered just enough tables to accommodate everyone coming to the junior-senior prom.

   B. bad because he ordered too few tables to accommodate everyone coming to the junior-senior prom.

   C. bad because he ordered more tables than were needed.

   D. good because he allowed for some extra seating for chaperones.

4. In a candy factory, 4 pieces of candy out of every *n* pieces tested are rejected, on the average. What fraction of those *n* pieces is <u>not</u> rejected?

   A. $\frac{n}{4}$

   B. $\frac{4}{n}$

   C. $\frac{n-4}{4}$

   D. $\frac{n-4}{n}$

Question 5 refers to a number cube like the one pictured to the right. Each face of the cube is labeled with just one of the digits 1, 2, 3, 4, 5, 6.

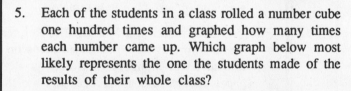

5. Each of the students in a class rolled a number cube one hundred times and graphed how many times each number came up. Which graph below most likely represents the one the students made of the results of their whole class?

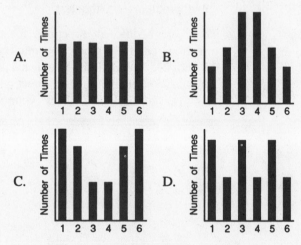

6. The width of this page is closest to

   A. 20 kilometers.

   B. 20 decimeters.

   C. 20 centimeters.

   D. 20 millimeters.

Question 7 refers to the airport shuttle schedule shown below.

Timetable: Departing Monmouth, Ocean, Union & Middlesex Counties
GOING TO: Newark International Airport

GOING TO NEWARK

		Berkeley Carteret – Asbury Pk $20.00	Fort Monmouth $15.00	Ramada Inn – West Long Branch $15.00	Sheraton – Eatontown $15.00	Appletown Inn – Eatontown $15.00	Marriot Residence – Eatontown $15.00	Tinton Falls – Hilton $15.00	Sunrise Suites – Tinton Falls $15.00	Envoy Inn – Tinton Falls $15.00	Marriot Courtyard – Red Bank $15.00	Molly Pitcher Inn – Red Bank $15.00	Bell Labs – Red Hill – Holmdel $15.00	Woodbridge Hilton $13.00	Airline Shuttle $13.00	Ramada Inn – Clark $12.00	Newark Airport	
Early Morning Red Eye		—	5:00	5:10	5:15	5:25	5:25	5:30	5:30	5:30	5:35	5:45	5:45	6:00	6:05	6:15	6:30	AM
	AM	6:45	7:00	7:10	7:15	7:25	7:25	7:30	7:30	7:30	7:35	7:45	7:45	8:00	8:05	8:15	8:30	AM
		8:45	9:00	9:10	9:15	9:25	9:25	9:30	9:30	9:30	9:35	9:45	9:45	10:00	10:05	10:15	10:30	
		10:45	11:00	11:10	11:15	11:25	11:25	11:30	11:30	11:30	11:35	11:45	11:45	12:00	12:05	12:15	12:30	
		12:45	1:00	1:10	1:15	1:25	1:25	1:30	1:30	1:30	1:35	1:45	1:45	2:00	2:05	2:15	2:30	
	PM	2:45	3:00	3:10	3:15	3:25	3:25	3:30	3:30	3:30	3:35	3:45	3:45	4:00	4:05	4:15	4:30	PM
		4:45	5:00	5:10	5:15	5:25	5:25	5:30	5:30	5:30	5:35	5:45	5:45	6:00	6:05	6:15	6:30	
		6:45	7:00	7:10	7:15	7:25	7:25	7:30	7:30	7:30	7:35	7:45	7:45	8:00	8:05	8:15	8:30	
		8:45	9:00	9:10	9:15	9:25	9:25	9:30	9:30	9:30	9:35	9:45	9:45	10:00	10:05	10:15	10:30	

7. Mrs. Wallenda lives at Fort Monmouth, New Jersey and must catch a plane scheduled to leave Newark Airport at 12:40 on a Wednesday afternoon. She must get to the airport at least 40 minutes before her flight time, but she absolutely refuses to wait around the airport any longer than necessary. At what time does the bus she should take depart from Fort Monmouth?

A. 8:45 a.m.

B. 9:00 a.m.

C. 10:45 a.m.

D. 11:00 a.m.

8. If each of the following procedures was applied to a given number, which of them would give equal results?
   I. subtract twice the number from itself
   II. divide one by the number
   III. multiply the number by – 1

A. I and II

B. II and III

C. I and III

D. I, II, and III

9. A warehouse manager's computer showed that there were 382 baseballs in stock. The baseballs were all in full boxes of 4 or 12. The manager claimed the computer's count was wrong. The manager was correct because 382 is not divisible by

A. 3.

B. 4.

C. 6.

D. 12.

10. Which of the following is NOT a way to find 125% of a number?

A. Multiply the number by 1.25.

B. Divide the number by 4 and add the result to the number.

C. Divide the number by 4 and multiply the result by 5.

D. Multiply the number by .25 and multiply the result by 4.

11. Three students started at the same flagpole in the middle of a large, flat grassy area and chose three different directions in which to walk. Each walked for 10 yards in a straight line away from that pole. Suppose many more students did this, each walking in a direction different from the directions chosen by all the others. If you think of the final positions of the students as being points, which of the following figures would contain all of those points?

A. circle

B. square

C. rhombus

D. triangle

3 **PLEASE GO ON TO THE NEXT PAGE →**

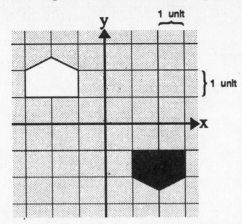

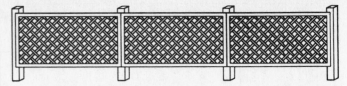

12. Performing which set of transformations on the white figure above will NOT result in the white figure covering the black figure completely?

    A. reflection in the y-axis followed by reflection in the x-axis

    B. translation 4 units to the right followed by reflection in the x-axis

    C. reflection in the y-axis followed by translation 4 units down

    D. rotation of 180° about the origin

13. Jane threw a dart that landed in the 3-point area of the target pictured below. Bill threw a dart that landed in its 1-point area.

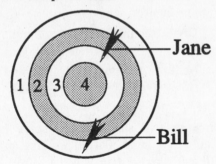

    Each of them has just one more dart to throw. It is now Jane's turn. In what area(s) of the target could Jane throw her dart so that she is sure to win, that is so that Bill's total points cannot tie or exceed her total points?

    A. in the 4-point area only

    B. in the 4-point or in the 3-point area only

    C. in the 4-point, in the 3-point, or in the 2-point area

    D. Jane cannot be sure she will win until after she and Bill both throw their darts.

14. The three individual sections of fence indicated in the drawing are each ten feet long and cost $98 each; posts cost $25 to $35 each. About how much would it cost to buy just enough of these sections and posts to build a 150-foot-long fence of the type pictured in the drawing?

    A. between $400 and $700

    B. between $800 and $1200

    C. between $1300 and $1600

    D. between $1800 and $2100

15. Suppose the 36 students in a junior class sold an average of 4.25 junior-class play tickets each. If each ticket to that play cost $4, how much money did those students bring in from their sale of tickets to that play?

    A. $144

    B. $153

    C. $612

    D. Not enough information is given.

16. It takes Brenda $\frac{3}{4}$ of an hour to cut her own lawn and $1\frac{1}{2}$ hours to cut her grandmother's lawn. Last summer, she cut her own lawn 4 times and her grandmother's 3 times. How many hours did she spend doing that cutting of lawns, if she always mows at the same rates as those indicated above?

    A. $5\frac{1}{4}$ hours

    B. 6 hours

    C. $7\frac{1}{2}$ hours

    D. $15\frac{3}{4}$ hours

4   **PLEASE GO ON TO THE NEXT PAGE** →

17. The Burger Baron Restaurant is open from 6 a.m. until midnight and serves all meals. Every half hour during an 8-hour period last Tuesday, Ronald counted the number of customers in that restaurant. He graphed his data but forgot to label the time-of-day axis.

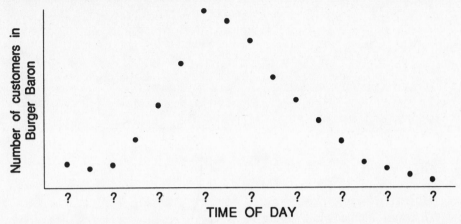

Which of the following time-of-day axes is most likely labeled the way it should have been in Ronald's graph?

A.

| 3 p.m. | 4 | 5 | 6 | 7 | 8 | 9 | 10 | 11 |

B.

| 10 a.m. | 11 | 12 p.m. | 1 | 2 | 3 | 4 | 5 | 6 |

C.

| 12 p.m. | 1 | 2 | 3 | 4 | 5 | 6 | 7 | 8 |

D.

| 6 a.m. | 7 | 8 | 9 | 10 | 11 | 12 p.m. | 1 | 2 |

18. Paula has an 8" x 16" picture which she glued onto a piece of matboard so that a 2-inch border of matboard was left showing all the way around her picture as indicated in the diagram below.

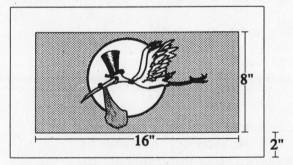

The cost of the matboard she used was $.02 per square inch. At this rate, what was the cost of the matboard indicated in the diagram above?

A. $2.24

B. $2.56

C. $3.60

D. $4.80

19. Which of the following points lies on the graph of $3x - y = 6$?

A. $(-1, -3)$

B. $(0, 6)$

C. $(1, -3)$

D. $(1, 3)$

20. Four friends are planning to eat at a restaurant where complete dinners cost between $12.00 and $17.00 per person. They want to leave the waiter a tip amounting to 15% of their total bill. Which of the following is the closest to what the four friends will need to leave for their combined total tip?

A. $2.00

B. $4.00

C. $9.00

D. $15.00

5   **PLEASE GO ON TO THE NEXT PAGE →**

21. Consider the number 36; some pairs of matching positive integer factors of 36 are (2,18), (3,12), (4,9), (6,6), ... (12,3), (18,2). Suppose someone graphs all possible pairs of matching positive integer factors of a given positive integer. Which of the following most likely represents such a graph?

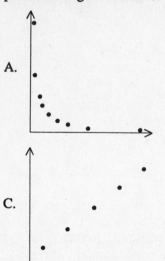

A.

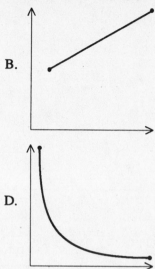

B.

C.

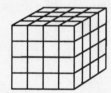

D.

DIRECTIONS FOR QUESTIONS 22 AND 23: These two questions are not multiple-choice. You are to encode your answers in the response grids provided for questions 22 and 23 in your answer folder. For each question, write your answer in the boxes at the top of the grid, one number (or decimal point) per box. Then fill in the corresponding circle below each box.

22. The large block pictured below is made up of 64 <u>unit</u> cubes.

The outside of the large block is painted. How many of the 64 unit cubes have paint on just one of their faces?

23. As music boxes come off an assembly line, inspectors check them for different reasons. Inspector A checks the 10th music box and every 10th one after that for the quality of the paint application; Inspector B checks the 25th music box and every 25th one after that for the quality of the gluing. Thus, a particular music box could be inspected as many as two times. If 3000 music boxes are produced one day, how many of them are inspected two times?

END OF PART 1 — You may check your work on this part only. Do not go on to the next part.

6

MATHEMATICS PART 2 — OPEN-ENDED QUESTIONS

DIRECTIONS: Give complete answers to all parts of both questions below. DO NOT DO YOUR WORK OR WRITE YOUR ANSWERS ON THIS TEST. No credit will be given for work written on this test. Show all your work and write your answers in the spaces provided for them on your answer sheet. You will be graded on the quality of your thinking, as reflected in your explanations, as well as on the correctness of your responses.

1. The Warlock Electronics Store advertises that it will never be undersold. The Warlock says that if you can find a lower regularly advertised price from another store for any item that Warlock sells, the Warlock will match that lower price and also give you an additional reduction that is 10 percent of the difference in the prices. Is the additional reduction significant? Present a convincing argument to support your answer; include a simple example as part of your argument.

2. The annual salaries of all the employees of a small company are listed below.

   President: $110,000

   Vice President: $60,000

   Senior Professionals: $50,000; $48,000; $48,000; $44,000

   Junior Professionals: $36,000; $36,000; $36,000; $32,000

   Clerical Staff: $22,000; $18,000; $14,000

   What are the mean, the median, and the mode of the salaries of the employees of this company? How is each of these statistics affected if one excludes the President's salary? What do your findings tell you about the statistic that should probably be used in discussions of the salary of a typical professional baseball player? Explain.

END OF PART 2 — You may check your work on this part or Part 1. DO NOT GO ON TO THE NEXT PART.

STOP

7

PART 1

1. (A) (B) (C) (D)
2. (A) (B) (C) (D)
3. (A) (B) (C) (D)
4. (A) (B) (C) (D)
5. (A) (B) (C) (D)
6. (A) (B) (C) (D)
7. (A) (B) (C) (D)
8. (A) (B) (C) (D)
9. (A) (B) (C) (D)
10. (A) (B) (C) (D)
11. (A) (B) (C) (D)
12. (A) (B) (C) (D)
13. (A) (B) (C) (D)
14. (A) (B) (C) (D)
15. (A) (B) (C) (D)
16. (A) (B) (C) (D)
17. (A) (B) (C) (D)
18. (A) (B) (C) (D)
19. (A) (B) (C) (D)
20. (A) (B) (C) (D)
21. (A) (B) (C) (D)

22.

2	4		
/	/	/	/
.	.	.	.
0	0	0	0
1	1	1	1
2	2	2	2
3	3	3	3
4	4	4	4
5	5	5	5
6	6	6	6
7	7	7	7
8	8	8	8
9	9	9	9

23.

6	0		
/	/	/	/
.	.	.	.
0	0	0	0
1	1	1	1
2	2	2	2
3	3	3	3
4	4	4	4
5	5	5	5
6	6	6	6
7	7	7	7
8	8	8	8
9	9	9	9

PART 2

1.

_____

2.

SCORING GUIDE 1:

3   A statement that additional reduction is not significant with explanation acknowledging that 10% of a <u>difference</u> is not that great **AND** specific appropriate example given/worked out **OR** reduction <u>is</u> significant with reasonable argument and example **OR** reduction <u>may be</u> significant with reasonable argument and examples showing both cases.

2   A focus on 10% of a difference but argument not convincing **OR** example not appropriate or lacking, or indication of significant/not significant missing.

1   A focus on 10% of a price, not 10% of a difference in prices, with statement of significance of reduction and example.

0   A focus on 10% of price and indication of not significant and/or no example **OR** blank or irrelevant or other incorrect response.

SCORING GUIDE 2:

3   Correct median ($36,000) and mode ($36,000) and correct process and reasonable value for mean ($42,615.38 or close)—(Error due to omission of data or minor computational error is acceptable.) **AND** correct effect on each statistic if President's salary is eliminated (median and mode unaffected and mean would decrease), **AND** indication that median or mode is better than the mean for discussion of salaries with reasonable explanation.

2   Two of the above requirements satisfactorily met and one missing or unsatisfactory; **OR** one requirement satisfactorily met and others partially satisfactory.

1   One requirement satisfactorily met, and others missing or unsatisfactory; **OR** two or three requirements partially satisfactory.

0   Unsatisfactory with respect to all three requirements **OR** blank or irrelevant or other incorrect response.

Grade 11
High School Proficiency Test
Sample Test 2

MATHEMATICS TEST

DIRECTIONS FOR MATHEMATICS PART 1

You will have 35 minutes to work on Part 1. Work carefully and try to get as many questions right as you can. Do not spend too much time on any one question. If you do not know an answer, make the best choice you can and go on to the next question.

You may use scratch paper or any space in the test booklet for working out your answers, but mark all of your answers on the Answer Folder. Mark only one answer for each question. If you make a mistake or wish to change an answer, be sure to erase your first choice completely.

You have received a Mathematics Reference Sheet which provides formulas and other useful information. Your reference sheet also includes a ruler requiring that a fold be made to create a good straightedge. You may use the information on this sheet to answer any of the test questions.

There are additional directions for the last two questions in Part 1. Follow these directions carefully when you mark your answers on the grids provided for questions 22 and 23. Work until you reach the end of Part 1. Please do not go on to Part 2 until you receive further directions. If you finish Part 1 before the time is up, you may go back and check your work.

MATHEMATICS PART 1

DIRECTIONS: Record your answer choices in the spaces provided for Mathematics Part 1 on your Answer Folder. Work each problem. Mark the letter for your answer in the appropriate space. UNLESS THE PROBLEM STATES OTHERWISE, DO NOT FIGURE SALES TAX IN YOUR ANSWERS TO PROBLEMS INVOLVING PURCHASES.

1. Which of the numbers below is NOT equal to the other three?

   A. $\sqrt{1.44}$

   B. 120%

   C. $\frac{12}{10}$

   D. 1.2×10^2

2. Which of these pieces of cardboard CANNOT be folded along the dotted lines to make a closed box?

   A.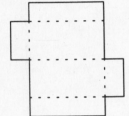

   B.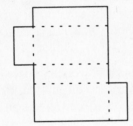

   C.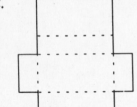

   D.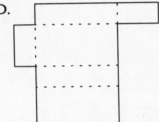

3. The fare for each taxi ride consists of a $3.00 initial charge and a charge of $1.20 per half-mile. At that rate, how much is the fare for a taxi ride of six miles?

   A. $10.20

   B. $17.40

   C. $25.20

   D. $32.40

Use this graph to answer question 4.

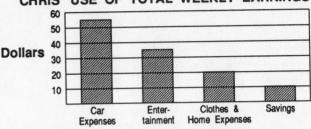

CHRIS' USE OF TOTAL WEEKLY EARNINGS

4. Approximately what percent of Chris' total weekly earnings is spent on entertainment?

   A. 20%

   B. 30%

   C. 40%

   D. 60%

5. Which of these sequences of steps transforms the equation $\frac{1}{2}x + 4 = 10$ into the equation $x = 12$?

   A. Subtract 4 from both sides and multiply both sides by 2.

   B. Multiply both sides by 2 and subtract 4 from both sides.

   C. Multiply both sides by $\frac{1}{2}$ and add 4 to both sides.

   D. Subtract 4 from both sides and divide both sides by 2.

6. When Mr. Chavez does the family marketing, he keeps in his head a running total of the prices of the items he puts in his shopping cart. The prices of the items in his cart are:

   $3.65 $11.98   43¢   43¢ $6.34 $2.99

   $2.99   23¢ $2.23 $6.49 $2.78 $14.29

   Estimate the total of the prices of those items. The total of the prices of those items is between _____.

   A. $30 and $40

   B. $40 and $50

   C. $50 and $60

   D. $60 and $70

2   **PLEASE GO ON TO THE NEXT PAGE →**

Use the figure below and the given information to answer question 7. Assume that the figure shows distances and angle measures that are drawn as accurately as possible.

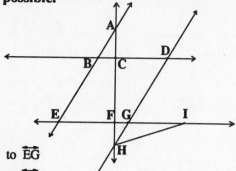

GIVEN:

$\overleftrightarrow{BD}$ is parallel to $\overleftrightarrow{EG}$

$\overleftrightarrow{AE}$ is parallel to $\overleftrightarrow{DH}$

$\overleftrightarrow{AH}$ is perpendicular to $\overleftrightarrow{BD}$

7. △ABC and △AEF are **not**

   A. right triangles.

   B. similar triangles.

   C. scalene triangles.

   D. congruent triangles.

8. The formula for changing temperature from Celsius to Fahrenheit is $F = \frac{9}{5}C + 32$. If the temperature of something is 60° C, what is its temperature in degrees Fahrenheit?

   A. 18.4° F

   B. 33.8° F

   C. 140° F

   D. 165.6° F

9. The number of Central High School students who gave to the United Fund this year was 342. This figure is 110% of what it was the previous year. This means that

   A. 10 more Central High School students gave to the United Fund.

   B. the number of Central High School students giving to the United Fund decreased from last year to this year.

   C. Central High School raised more money for the United Fund this year than it did last year.

   D. the number of Central High School students giving to the United Fund increased from last year to this year.

10. There are 5 teams in a volleyball league. Every team in that league plays every other team in that league exactly once. Which of the figures below would be most helpful in determining how many games the teams in that league played?

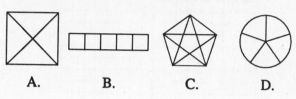

   A.   B.   C.   D.

11. Three high schools are particularly proud of their driver-education programs. The table below shows the number of students in each school's driver-education program last year and the number of students who passed their driver's test on the first try last year.

School	number of students	students passing on first try
Polk School	50	42
Guzzetti Memorial	90	81
Washington Central	72	66

Which school's driver-education program was most successful in getting its students to pass their driver's test on their first try?

   A. Polk School

   B. Guzzetti Memorial

   C. Washington Central

   D. There is a tie.

12. The diameter of a full-sized automobile steering wheel is probably closest to

   A. 3.5 cm.

   B. 35 cm.

   C. 350 cm.

   D. 3500 cm.

3   **PLEASE GO ON TO THE NEXT PAGE →**

13. Plot the points A(−2,⁺3) and B(⁺6,−3) on the grid below.

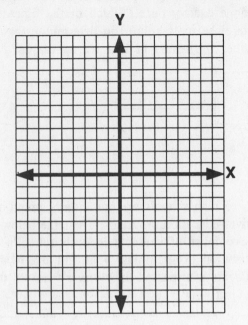

What is the length of $\overline{AB}$?

A.   7 units
B.   9 units
C.   10 units
D.   14 units

14. The table below indicates a linear relationship between a and b.

a	b
0	1
2	5
4	□
6	13
8	17

According to this pattern, which of the following numbers belongs in the box in the table?

A.   7
B.   9
C.   10
D.   11

15. Which of the following graphs most likely shows an automobile's resale value plotted against its age?

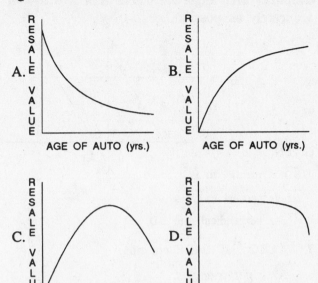

16. Mrs. Robinson purchased a new car for $8800 plus 6% sales tax. How much more would she have paid for that car if the sales tax were 7% instead of 6%?

A. $88
B. $198
C. $528
D. $616

Use this diagram to answer question 17.

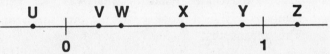

17. Which point on the number line above could represent the product of the numbers represented by **W** and **X**?

A.   U
B.   V
C.   Y
D.   Z

4   **PLEASE GO ON TO THE NEXT PAGE →**

Use this diagram to answer question 18.

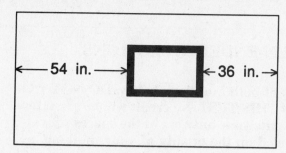

18. As shown in this diagram, the picture is not centered on the wall from left to right. How far to the left should it be moved to be centered?

   A. 9 inches
   B. 18 inches
   C. 27 inches
   D. Not enough information is given.

19. Sally is running a game booth at the school fair. She carefully collects exactly 30 cents from every player. At the end of the fair, she must count the money collected. She counts it four times, getting a different total each time. Which of the following could be the correct total?

   A. $22.45
   B. $22.50
   C. $22.60
   D. $22.65

20. Which of the following equations represents the line containing the points given in the diagram below.

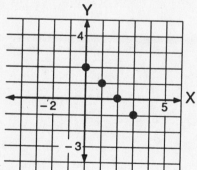

   A. $y = x + 2$
   B. $y = x - 2$
   C. $y = -x$
   D. $y = 2 - x$

21. A very small stone is somewhere in a bucket of sawdust. The weight of the sawdust by itself is 50 ounces. If a full scoop holds 5 ounces of sawdust, what is the probability of getting that stone by taking 2 full scoops of sawdust out of the bucket?

   A. .10
   B. .20
   C. .40
   D. Cannot determine from weights.

DIRECTIONS FOR QUESTIONS 22 AND 23: These two questions are not multiple-choice. You are to encode your answers in the response grids provided for questions 22 and 23 in your Answer Folder. For each question, write your answer in the boxes at the top of the grid, one number (or decimal point) per box. Then fill in the corresponding circle below each box.

Use this diagram to answer question 22.

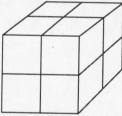

22. The block sketched above is 2 inches by 2 inches by 2 inches and weighs 32 ounces. What would be the weight of a block of the same material that is 4 inches by 4 inches by 4 inches?

23. Each month, Wilma earns $25 from a part-time job. She puts $18 of it into a savings account and the remaining $7 of it into her checking account. Suppose she deposits no money from other sources and withdraws no money from either account. By the time she has deposited $126 into her checking account, how much will she have put into her savings account?

END OF PART 1 — You may check your work on this part only. Do not go on to the next part.

5

MATHEMATICS PART 2 — OPEN-ENDED QUESTIONS

DIRECTIONS: Give complete answers to all parts of both questions below. DO NOT DO YOUR WORK OR WRITE YOUR ANSWERS ON THIS TEST. No credit will be given for work written on this test. Show all your work and write your answers in the spaces provided for them on your answer sheet. You will be graded on the quality of your thinking, as reflected in your explanations, as well as on the correctness of your responses.

1. Estimate 97.85 x 209 **in your head**. Explain in writing what your estimate is and how you got it.

2. The math exam scores for the 21 students in Mr. Walker's homeroom were:

65	90	82	78	84	92	88	86	70	68	75
88	90	85	61	81	79	82	84	83	90	

    a. The mean or average of the above scores is 81. What is the median score? What is the mode?

    b. Use the grid on your answer sheet to make a bar graph showing the frequency or number of scores in each of the score ranges 60-64, 65-69, 70-74, etc.

    c. Which is the best general indicator of this class's performance on the exam — the mean, median, or mode? Explain your answer.

STOP

END OF PART 2 — You may check your work on this part or Part 1. DO NOT GO ON TO THE NEXT PART.

6

PART 1

1. Ⓐ Ⓑ Ⓒ **●D**
2. **●A** Ⓑ Ⓒ Ⓓ
3. Ⓐ **●B** Ⓒ Ⓓ
4. Ⓐ **●B** Ⓒ Ⓓ
5. **●A** Ⓑ Ⓒ Ⓓ
6. Ⓐ Ⓑ **●C** Ⓓ
7. Ⓐ Ⓑ Ⓒ **●D**
8. Ⓐ Ⓑ **●C** Ⓓ
9. Ⓐ Ⓑ Ⓒ **●D**
10. Ⓐ Ⓑ **●C** Ⓓ
11. Ⓐ Ⓑ **●C** Ⓓ
12. Ⓐ **●B** Ⓒ Ⓓ
13. Ⓐ Ⓑ **●C** Ⓓ
14. Ⓐ **●B** Ⓒ Ⓓ
15. **●A** Ⓑ Ⓒ Ⓓ
16. **●A** Ⓑ Ⓒ Ⓓ
17. Ⓐ **●B** Ⓒ Ⓓ
18. **●A** Ⓑ Ⓒ Ⓓ
19. Ⓐ **●B** Ⓒ Ⓓ
20. Ⓐ Ⓑ Ⓒ **●D**
21. Ⓐ **●B** Ⓒ Ⓓ

22.

2	5	6	
/	/	/	/
.	.	.	.
0	0	0	0
1	1	1	1
●2	2	2	2
3	3	3	3
4	4	4	4
5	●5	5	5
6	6	●6	6
7	7	7	7
8	8	8	8
9	9	9	9

23.

3	2	4	
/	/	/	/
.	.	.	.
0	0	0	0
1	1	1	1
2	●2	2	2
●3	3	3	3
4	4	●4	4
5	5	5	5
6	6	6	6
7	7	7	7
8	8	8	8
9	9	9	9

PART 2

1.

2.

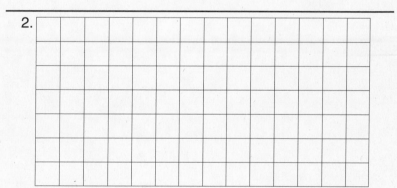

SCORING GUIDE 1:

3   A clear explanation of a method that can easily be done mentally (for example 100×200, 100×205, 90×200) and an answer that is consistent with the explanation **OR** an explanation of a more complex multiplication with some prerounding and no indication that the multiplication was not done mentally.

2   The numbers are rounded first but the computation does not match the explanation **OR** the numbers are rounded then added.

1   The numbers are rounded first but not enough to make computation easy **AND** there is an explanation but no answer or the computation is shown.

0   The product is computed exactly **OR** there is an incorrect response.

SCORING GUIDE 2:

3   Student answers (a) correctly (median – 83, mode – 90), presents an accurate graph for (b), and chooses the median as the best general indicator for (c), **AND** work is clear.

2   Student answers (a), (b), and (c) correctly but work is unclear **OR** answers (a) and (b) correctly but (c) is incorrect, work is clear **OR** answers (a), (b), and/or (c) incorrectly due to minor computational errors, work is clear.

1   Student answers (a), (b), and (c) incorrectly due to major computational errors **OR** answers parts of (a), (b), and (c) correctly but work missing.

0   The student answers inappropriately or fails to attempt an answer.

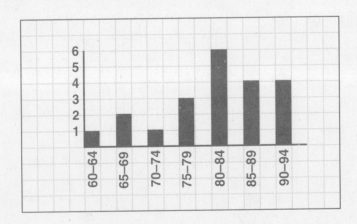

Grade 11
High School Proficiency Test
Sample Test 3

MATHEMATICS TEST

DIRECTIONS FOR MATHEMATICS PART 1

You will have 35 minutes to work on Part 1. Work carefully and try to get as many questions right as you can. Do not spend too much time on any one question. If you do not know an answer, make the best choice you can and go on to the next question.

You may use scratch paper or any space in the test booklet for working out your answers, but mark all of your answers on the Answer Folder. Mark only one answer for each question. If you make a mistake or wish to change an answer, be sure to erase your first choice completely.

You have received a Mathematics Reference Sheet which provides formulas and other useful information. Your reference sheet also includes a ruler requiring that a fold be made to create a good straightedge. You may use the information on this sheet to answer any of the test questions.

There are additional directions for the last two questions in Part 1. Follow these directions carefully when you mark your answers on the grids provided for questions 22 and 23. Work until you reach the end of Part 1. Please do not go on to Part 2 until you receive further directions. If you finish Part 1 before the time is up, you may go back and check your work.

MATHEMATICS PART 1

DIRECTIONS: Record your answer choices in the spaces provided for Mathematics Part 1 on your Answer Folder. Work each problem. Mark the letter for your answer in the appropriate space. UNLESS THE PROBLEM STATES OTHERWISE, DO NOT FIGURE SALES TAX IN YOUR ANSWERS TO PROBLEMS INVOLVING PURCHASES.

1. In which list are the units of measurement arranged in order from LEAST to GREATEST?

   A. quart, pint, gallon

   B. pint, quart, gallon

   C. pint, gallon, quart

   D. quart, gallon, pint

Use this diagram to answer question 2.

2. The large cube shown above has had some small cubes removed from it. How many, in all, have been removed?

   A. 5

   B. 6

   C. 7

   D. 8

3. The table below indicates a relationship between a and b.

a	b
0	− 2
1	1
2	4
⋮	⋮
5	13
⋮	⋮
8	22

   Which of the equations below expresses the relationship between a and b that is indicated in the table?

   A. $b = a^2$

   B. $b = 2a + 3$

   C. $b = 3a - 2$

   D. $b = a + 3$

4. Maggie and Keith are starting to save money for a car. Maggie saves $120 each month, and Keith saves $80 each month. At this rate, after how many months will Maggie have saved exactly $1000 more than Keith?

   A. 5 months

   B. 10 months

   C. 20 months

   D. 25 months

5. To find out if a particular area is generally above or below sea level, a geologist checked the elevation at several places in the area. She obtained the following results relative to sea level measured to the nearest foot; positive numbers represent distance above sea level and negative numbers represent distance below sea level:

   +3, +5, − 3, +1, − 4, − 2, +1, − 3, − 4, − 4.

   What is the area's average elevation?

   A. − 10 feet

   B. − 1 foot

   C. 0 feet

   D. +10 feet

Use the graph below to answer question 6.

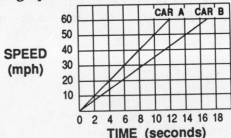

6. Based on the graph above, which car takes the least amount of time to go from 0 to 60 mph and about how much less time does it take?

   A. Car A by about 5 seconds

   B. Car B by about 5 seconds

   C. Car A by about $2\frac{1}{2}$ seconds

   D. Car B by about $2\frac{1}{2}$ seconds

2   **PLEASE GO ON TO THE NEXT PAGE →**

7. Plot the following points on the grid below:

A(-7,+3) B(+5,+8) C(+5,-2)

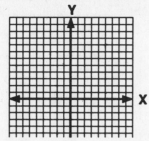

Triangle ABC is _____ triangle.

Which of the following choices can be used in the blank above to give a correct statement?

A. a right

B. an obtuse

C. an equilateral

D. an isosceles

8. The baselines of a baseball diamond form a square with side lengths of 90 feet.

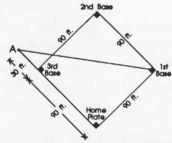

A player catches a ball at point A which is on the foul line 30 feet beyond 3rd base. How far from first base is the player when he catches the ball?

A. 120 ft.

B. 150 ft.

C. 180 ft.

D. 210 ft.

9. Which of these is one way to find $\frac{5}{8}$ of a number?

A. Multiply the number by $\frac{8}{5}$.

B. Divide the number by 5 and divide the result by 8.

C. Divide the number by 5 and multiply the result by 8.

D. Divide the number by 8 and multiply the result by 5.

10. The graph below represents Jane's car trip from Weston to Berryville.

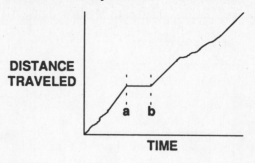

Which of the following is most likely to have happened between time a and time b?

A. Jane stopped for a meal.

B. Jane's car was moving slowly.

C. Jane stopped her car several times at traffic signals.

D. Jane was driving fast on the turnpike.

11. For a sale, a shopkeeper lowers the original price of an item by 20 percent. After the sale, the shopkeeper raised the price of that item by 20 percent of its sale price. The price of the item then is

A. more than the original price.

B. less than the original price.

C. the same as the original price.

D. There is not enough information to compare the two prices.

12. Which spinner below would give you the best chance of spinning a 3? (The spinners are drawn actual size.)

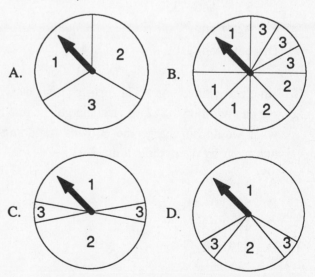

3   PLEASE GO ON TO THE NEXT PAGE →

13. While interviewing students at Washington High School, Paul asked 20 students (picked at random) what their favorite fall sport is. Maria asked 50 different students (picked at random) the same question. George combined Paul's data and Maria's data. All three graphed their results:

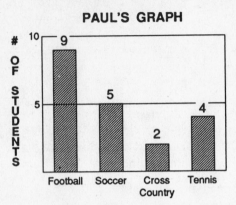

PAUL'S GRAPH

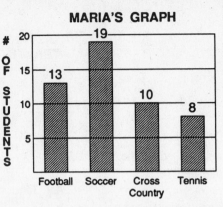

MARIA'S GRAPH

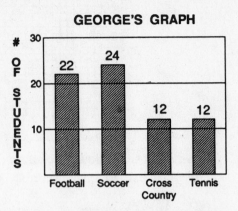

GEORGE'S GRAPH

Which of these graphs could be used to give the **most reliable** estimate of the percentage of the Washington High School student population whose favorite fall sport is soccer?

A. Paul's

B. Maria's

C. George's

D. There is no reason to use one graph rather than another.

14. Last week, Georgette earned $360. As part of estimating the amount of her paycheck, she first adds and then rounds to the nearest percent the deductions indicated below:

Federal Income Tax: 15.0%
FICA (Social Security): 7.5%
Unemployment Insurance: .... .25%
State Income Tax: 2.5%

Her estimate of the amount of her paycheck is between _____.

A. $350 and $400

B. $300 and $350

C. $250 and $300

D. $50 and $100

15. An electrician charges $24 for each hour he works plus an additional $12 service charge. At that rate, what would he charge the Browns for doing $3\frac{1}{2}$ hours of work at their home?

A. $39.50

B. $66.00

C. $96.00

D. $291.50

16. Suppose that each time a ball bounces, it goes up $\frac{1}{2}$ the distance it fell. If that ball is dropped from a height of x feet, which of these expressions represents the total distance it has traveled when it hits the floor for the fifth time?

A. $x + \frac{1}{2} + \frac{1}{4} + \frac{1}{8} + \frac{1}{16}$

B. $x + \frac{1}{2} + \frac{1}{2} + \frac{1}{4} + \frac{1}{4} + \frac{1}{8} + \frac{1}{8} + \frac{1}{16} + \frac{1}{16}$

C. $x + \frac{x}{2} + \frac{x}{2} + \frac{x}{4} + \frac{x}{4} + \frac{x}{8} + \frac{x}{8} + \frac{x}{16} + \frac{x}{16}$

D. $(x)(\frac{1}{2})(\frac{1}{4})(\frac{1}{8})(\frac{1}{16})$

17. When purchasing an item, Nick gave a sales clerk a 20-dollar bill. The clerk gave him the item and change consisting of d dollar bills, q quarters, and n nickels. Which of the following expressions represents the cost in dollars of the item?

A. $20 - (d + q + n)$

B. $20 - d - .25q - .05n$

C. $d + q + n$

D. $100d + 25q + 5n$

4   PLEASE GO ON TO THE NEXT PAGE →

Use this diagram to answer question 18.

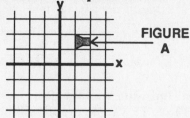

FIGURE
A

18. Which of the following represents the result of reflecting figure A in the y-axis and then reflecting that image in the x-axis?

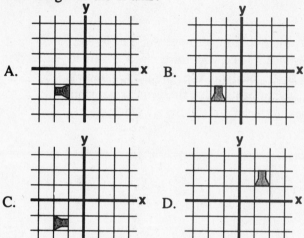

A.   B.

C.   D.

19. The figure below shows a circle of radius r inside a square of side length 2r.

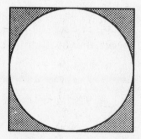

In terms of r, what is the area of the shaded region inside the square and outside the circle?

A. $4r^2 - \pi r^2$

B. $4 - \pi$

C. $r^2 - \pi r^2$

D. $4\pi r^2$

Use this diagram to answer question 20.

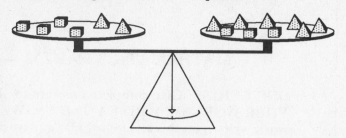

20. What is the weight of one of the cubes if each pyramid weighs 2 pounds?

A. $\frac{1}{4}$ pound

B. 4 pounds

C. 6 pounds

D. 8 pounds

21. There are 20 students in a class. The average grade for that class on a test was computed as 74, but one student's grade was read mistakenly as 50 instead of 90. What will the average grade for that class be when it is recomputed using the corrected score?

A. 76

B. 78.5

C. 114

D. Not enough information is given.

DIRECTIONS FOR QUESTIONS 22 AND 23: These two questions are not multiple-choice. You are to encode your answers in the response grids provided for questions 22 and 23 in your Answer Folder. For each question, write your answer in the boxes at the top of the grid, one number (or decimal point) per box. Then fill in the corresponding circle below each box.

22. The scale on a map is $\frac{1}{2}$ inch = 20 miles. How far apart are two cities that are shown as being 5 inches apart on that map?

23. Howard drove his car 285 miles. It used $12\frac{1}{2}$ gallons of gasoline. How many miles per gallon did he get on that trip?

END OF PART 1 — You may check your work on this part only. DO NOT GO ON TO THE NEXT PART.

5

STOP

MATHEMATICS PART 2 — OPEN-ENDED QUESTIONS

DIRECTIONS: Give complete answers to all parts of both questions below. DO NOT DO YOUR WORK OR WRITE YOUR ANSWERS ON THIS TEST. No credit will be given for work written on this test. Show all your work and write your answers in the spaces provided for them on your answer sheet. You will be graded on the quality of your thinking, as reflected in your explanations, as well as on the correctness of your responses.

1. Sketch the figure below in the space for this question on your Answer Folder. Use the ruler on the Mathematics Reference Sheet you have been given to determine the lengths of the sides of the figure below. Label the corresponding sides of your sketch with the measurements you find. Use these measurements to find the perimeter and the area of the figure below. Show all work clearly on your Answer Folder.

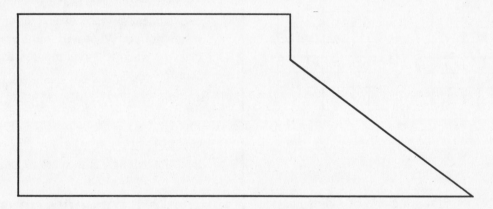

2. On the grid on your answer sheet, draw a triangle and a rectangle each of which has an area of 16 square units. (Use the straight edge on the Mathematics Reference Sheet you have been given.)

END OF PART 2 — You may check your work on this part or Part 1. DO NOT GO ON TO THE NEXT PART.

STOP

6

PART 1

1. (A) **(B)** (C) (D)

2. (A) (B) **(C)** (D)

3. (A) (B) **(C)** (D)

4. (A) (B) (C) **(D)**

5. (A) **(B)** (C) (D)

6. **(A)** (B) (C) (D)

7. (A) (B) (C) **(D)**

8. (A) **(B)** (C) (D)

9. (A) (B) (C) **(D)**

10. **(A)** (B) (C) (D)

11. (A) **(B)** (C) (D)

12. **(A)** (B) (C) (D)

13. (A) (B) **(C)** (D)

14. (A) (B) **(C)** (D)

15. (A) (B) **(C)** (D)

16. (A) (B) **(C)** (D)

17. (A) **(B)** (C) (D)

18. **(A)** (B) (C) (D)

19. **(A)** (B) (C) (D)

20. (A) (B) (C) **(D)**

21. **(A)** (B) (C) (D)

22.

2	0	0	
/	/	/	/
.	.	.	.
0	**0**	**0**	0
1	1	1	1
2	2	2	2
3	3	3	3
4	4	4	4
5	5	5	5
6	6	6	6
7	7	7	7
8	8	8	8
9	9	9	9

23.

2	2	.	8
/	/	/	/
.	.	**.**	.
0	0	0	0
1	1	1	1
2	**2**	2	2
3	3	3	3
4	4	4	4
5	5	5	5
6	6	6	6
7	7	7	7
8	8	8	**8**
9	9	9	9

PART 2

1.

2.

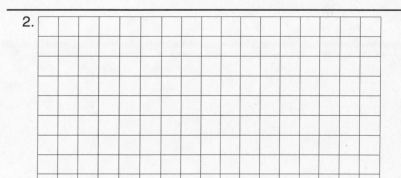

SCORING GUIDE 1:

3   Correctly labels lengths in sketch (accept all reasonable measurements) and determines correct perimeter and area based on lengths given by student **AND** work is shown.

2   Correctly labels lengths and gives correct perimeter and area but work is weak or unclear **OR** labels lengths correctly but gives incorrect area and/or perimeter due to minor computational errors **OR** incorrecly labels the lengths but calculates the perimeter and area using the correct formulas.

1   Correctly labels the lengths but gives incorrect perimeter and area due to major errors **OR** correctly labels the lengths but does not give perimeter and area **OR** gives correct answers but does not show work.

0   The student answers inappropriately or fails to attempt an answer.

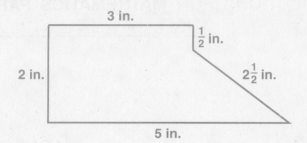

SCORING GUIDE 2:

3   The student correctly draws both triangle and rectangle each with area 16 square units.

2   The student draws only one figure with the correct area **OR** draws both figures inaccurately but labels them so that the areas are both 16 square units.

1   The student draws both figures incorrectly.

0   The student answers inappropriately or fails to attempt an answer.

Grade 11
High School Proficiency Test
Sample Test 4

MATHEMATICS SECTION

DIRECTIONS FOR MATHEMATICS PART 1

You will have 35 minutes to work on Part 1. Work carefully and try to answer as many questions right as you can. Do not spend too much time on any one question. If you do not know an answer, make the best choice you can and go on to the next question.

You may use scratch paper or any space in the test booklet for working out your answers, but mark all of your answers on your answer folder. Mark only one answer for each question. If you make a mistake or wish to change an answer, be sure to erase your first choice completely.

You have received a Mathematics Reference Sheet which provides formulas and other useful information. Open-ended items on some forms of the test will require that you fold and tear along the perforations at the bottom of your reference sheet to make paper geometric shapes. You may use the information on the reference sheet to help solve problems on the test.

There are additional directions for the last two questions in Part 1. Follow these directions carefully when you mark your answers on the grids provided for questions 22 and 23. Work until you reach the end of Part 1. Please do not go on to Part 2 until you receive further directions. If you finish Part 1 before the time is up, you may go back and check your work.

MATHEMATICS PART 1

DIRECTIONS: Work all problems. Record your answer choices in the spaces provided for Mathematics Part 1 on your answer folder. Mark the letter for your answer in the appropriate space. UNLESS THE PROBLEM STATES OTHERWISE, DO NOT FIGURE SALES TAX IN YOUR ANSWERS TO PROBLEMS INVOLVING PURCHASES.

1. This year the number of seniors taking mathematics is 5 percent greater than it was last year. If there were 40 seniors taking mathematics last year, how many seniors are taking mathematics this year?

   A. 42
   B. 45
   C. 48
   D. 60

Use the table below to answer question 2.

CLASS	AMOUNT RAISED	CLASS	AMOUNT RAISED
Seniors	$235	Sophomores	$215
Juniors	$208	Freshman	$148

2. The classes in a high school raised the amounts shown above for charity. Four students started to construct a bar graph showing this information. Which of the following four approaches to beginning the graph is most likely to be easiest to interpret?

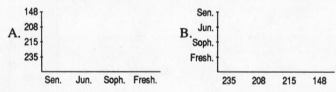

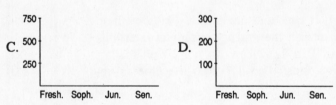

3. A house painter uses the following formula to determine how much to charge for doing a job. C is the total charge in dollars, and h is the number of hours of work required to complete the job.

   $$C = 24h + 12$$

   This formula indicates that for every additional hour the house painter works, the total charge is increased by

   A. $12.
   B. $24.
   C. $36.
   D. $288.

Refer to the figure below to answer question 4.

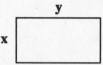

4. Which of the following formulas correctly represents the perimeter of the rectangle pictured above?

   I. $x + y + x + y$
   II. $2x + 2y$
   III. xy
   IV. $4xy$

   A. I only
   B. III only
   C. I and II only
   D. II and IV only

5. Which of the following is NOT a characteristic of all parallelograms?

   A. Diagonals are perpendicular.
   B. Diagonals bisect each other.
   C. Opposite angles are equal.
   D. Opposite sides are equal.

Use the mileage chart below to answer question 6.

Mileage Between Principal Cities	Atlantic City	Bridgeton	Camden	Cape May	Cherry Hill	Easton, PA	Elizabeth	Jersey City	Long Branch	Newark	New Brunswick	New York, NY	Paterson	Trenton
Atlantic City		81	57	48	55	115	105	119	83	108	93	130	123	74
Camden	57	40		84	9	57	81	85	81	84	56	104	99	32
Newark	108	116	84	154	80	66	8	6	48		23	27	15	50
Paterson	123	131	99	165	95	63	23	21	63	15	38	32		84
Trenton	74	70	32	106	35	52	48	56	48	50	28	74	84	
New Brunswick	93	99	56	128	58	45	26	31	40	23		46	38	28

6. Newark, New Jersey and Cape May, New Jersey are connected by major highways. Approximately how long would it take to drive from Newark to Cape May in traffic that averages 55 miles per hour?

   A. $1\frac{1}{2}$ hours
   B. 2 hours
   C. 3 hours
   D. 4 hours

2   **PLEASE GO ON TO THE NEXT PAGE →**

7. A plane passing through a solid gives you a cross section of the solid. For example, the cross section of a solid pyramid shown below is a triangular region. (See shaded figure.)

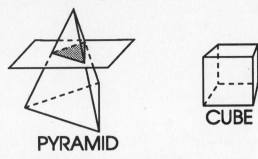

PYRAMID CUBE

Which of the following plane figures CANNOT be a cross section of a solid cube?

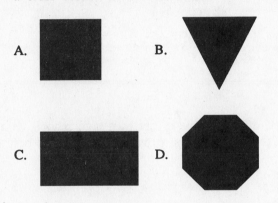

A. B. C. D.

8. John has a 10-question quiz on Friday. His father agrees to give him on Saturday his regular $5 allowance plus 75 cents for each question he answered correctly on Friday's quiz. However, he will not give John any more than twice his weekly allowance. Which inequality below accurately represents the situation described above?

A. $.75n \leq 10$
B. $5 - .75n \leq 10$
C. $.75n + 5 \leq 10$
D. $(.75 + 5)n \leq 10$

9. Which of the following is a first step in finding the median of a set of numbers?

A. Find the sum of the numbers.
B. List the numbers in numerical order.
C. Look for the most frequently occurring number.
D. Divide each number by the number of terms.

10. Which graph below shows the relationship between speed in miles per hour and speed in kilometers per hour?

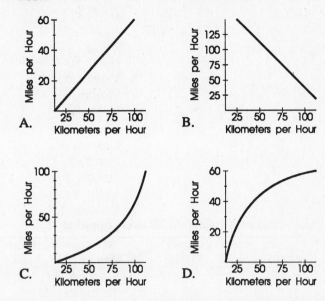

11. In a neighborhood contest, each contestant threw a heavy weight three times. Ralph threw the weight 8 ft. 9 in., then 10 ft. 6 in., and then 11 ft. 2 in. What was the combined distance of Ralph's throws?

A. 30.7 ft.
B. 29.17 ft.
C. 30 ft. 7 in.
D. 30 ft. 5 in.

12. The general partners in a small company, Miranda, Cohen, and Brown, share its profits in the ratio of 3:2:5, respectively. If that company's profits amount to $24,300 this year, what is Mr. Miranda's share?

A. $2,430
B. $7,290
C. $8,100
D. $14,580

3 **PLEASE GO ON TO THE NEXT PAGE →**

13. The students who took the written driver's test at a particular testing center one day were from three different high schools. Their test scores are given below.

NAME	SCHOOL	SCORE
Adams, J.	Gunnison	62
Baker, P.	Taylor	76
Chin, H.	Gunnison	87
Drabowski, C.	Braddock	79
Elmore, J.	Taylor	64
Ferris, W.	Braddock	83
Garver, G.	Gunnison	81
Greer, P.	Braddock	84
Harris, R.	Gunnison	92
Jacoby, P.	Taylor	92
Kelly, M.	Braddock	88
Lassiter, L.	Braddock	94
Martin, S.	Gunnison	82
Petrocelli, R.	Gunnison	74
Ramirez, R.	Taylor	84
Saunders, M.	Taylor	80
Thompson, L.	Braddock	89
Wilson, P.	Gunnison	90

All these students participated in the driver's education program offered in his or her own high school. Based on the students' test scores, which school's driver's education program appears to prepare its students best for the written driver's test?

A. Braddock

B. Gunnison

C. Taylor

D. Two schools appear to prepare their students equally well.

14. From the four types of boxes pictured below, you must choose a type of box to hold exactly one dozen blocks of cheese; each of the cheese blocks is a rectangular parallelepiped which is 1 inch by 2 inches by 6 inches. The measurements shown for each type of box are its interior dimensions. Which type of box must you choose to minimize the amount of unfilled space left inside the box after it has been packed with cheese blocks?

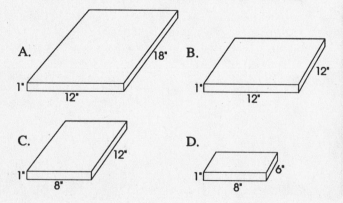

15. If $3y - 5 = 2 + 14y$, then $y =$

A. $-\dfrac{7}{11}$

B. $-\dfrac{3}{17}$

C. $\dfrac{3}{17}$

D. $\dfrac{7}{11}$

16. On some days, a history teacher has the students in a particular class work in groups of 4, on other days in groups of 6 or 8. However, when all students are present, there is always one student left over after the groups are formed. Which of the following could be the number of students in that class?

A. 37

B. 33

C. 29

D. 25

4   **PLEASE GO ON TO THE NEXT PAGE →**

17. You are playing a game in which you move a chip on a number line. Where you move the chip is determined by the cards you draw from a pack. Each card has an integer printed on it. Your chip is now at the position shown below.

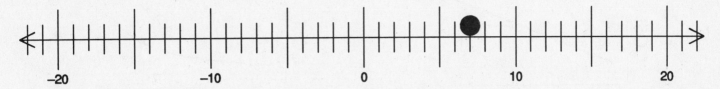

-20   -10   0   10   20

On each turn, you move your chip to the location with the coordinate equal to the sum of the coordinate of your current location and the number on the card you draw. Suppose you draw cards with the following sequence of numbers: $-2, 6, -7, -12, -4$. What is the coordinate of the location of your chip after you complete this sequence of moves?

A. 12
B. 11
C. -12
D. -19

18. To solve a science problem, Luis has to convert 70 miles per hour to an equivalent number of feet per second. Approximately which of these answers does he get when he performs the operations indicated below?

$$\frac{70 \text{ miles}}{1 \text{ hour}} \times \frac{5280 \text{ feet}}{1 \text{ mile}} \times \frac{1 \text{ hour}}{60 \text{ minutes}} \times \frac{1 \text{ minute}}{60 \text{ seconds}}$$

A. 10 feet per second
B. 50 feet per second
C. 100 feet per second
D. 200 feet per second

19. According to the weather channel, there is a 50% chance of rain for each of the next four days. If this is true, what is the probability that it will rain on <u>at least one</u> of those days?

A. greater than 50%
B. 50%
C. less than 50%
D. You cannot tell.

20. A car traveled 8 miles in 12 minutes. What was its average speed for that trip?

A. 1.5 miles per hour
B. 40 miles per hour
C. 60 miles per hour
D. 96 miles per hour

21. Suppose the U.S. Post Office has proposed increasing the cost of first-class postage to 30 cents for the first ounce or fraction thereof and 26 cents for each additional ounce or fraction thereof. Which of the graphs below best represents the cost of mailing a first-class item depending on the weight of that item in ounces?

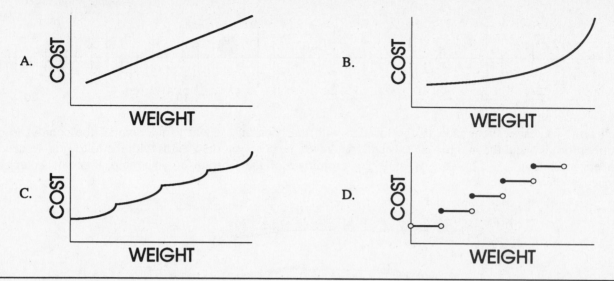

DIRECTIONS FOR QUESTIONS 22 AND 23: These two questions are not multiple-choice. You are to encode your answers in the response grids provided for questions 22 and 23 in your answer folder. For each question, write your answer in the boxes at the top of the grid, one number (or decimal point) per box. Then fill in the corresponding circle below each box.

22. A rectangular solid can be covered with exactly 88 square inches of material. If a second rectangular solid has dimensions exactly twice those of the first rectangular solid, what is the least number of square inches of the same material which would cover it in the same way as the first one?

23. The triangular pattern of numbers below has some interesting characteristics. Except for the 1s, each number is the sum of the two numbers diagonally above it.

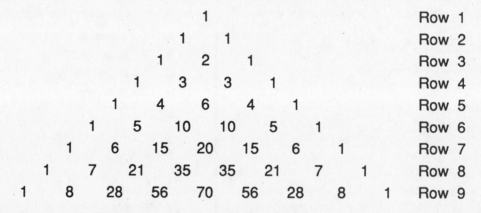

				1					Row 1
			1		1				Row 2
		1		2		1			Row 3
	1		3		3		1		Row 4
1		4		6		4		1	Row 5

Row 6: 1 5 10 10 5 1
Row 7: 1 6 15 20 15 6 1
Row 8: 1 7 21 35 35 21 7 1
Row 9: 1 8 28 56 70 56 28 8 1

What is the sum of the numbers in the 11th row? (HINT: Determine the pattern followed by the sums of the numbers in each row.)

END OF PART 1 – You may check your work on this part only. DO NOT GO ON TO THE NEXT PART.

6

MATHEMATICS PART 2 — OPEN-ENDED QUESTIONS

DIRECTIONS: Give complete answers to all parts of both questions below. DO NOT DO YOUR WORK OR WRITE YOUR ANSWERS ON THIS TEST. No credit will be given for work written on this test. Show all your work and write your answers in the spaces provided for them on your answer sheet. You will be graded on the quality of your thinking, as reflected in your explanations, as well as on the correctness of your responses.

Use the picture below to answer question 1.

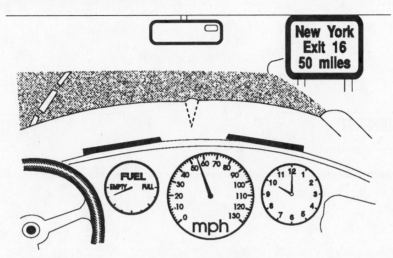

1. Suppose you are driving on the New Jersey Turnpike to go to a new job interview in New York at 11:30 a.m. You know that you can average 55 mph on the turnpike. You must drive 50 miles to the exit you must use; it will take about 25 more minutes of driving to get to the location of your appointment after you leave the turnpike. You also know that the gas tank holds 20 gallons and that you get about 18 miles per gallon on the highway.

   Based only on this information and the information in the picture above, do you need to stop and buy gasoline on the way to New York? If you do stop to buy gasoline, remember it will take some time to do so. Will you make it to your appointment early, on time, or late? If early or late, about how early or late would you expect to be? Explain your answers carefully.

2. Make one large square region, one small square region, and two rectangular regions by folding and tearing your reference sheet along the perforations. Let x stand for the side length of the larger square region and assume that the small square region has side length one. (The side lengths are shown on the paper geometric shapes that you will make.)

   Form a square region by putting all of those shapes together so that they lie flat. Except for vertices and edges, no part of any of the shapes may cover a part of another of the shapes. In the space provided in your answer folder, sketch a picture of the region you have formed. Include in your sketch the outlines of the pieces you fitted together to form the region. Express the perimeter and area of the square region that you formed in terms of the dimensions and areas of the four pieces you fitted together to make it. Be sure that your sketch shows clearly the information you used in responding to this item.

END OF PART 2 – You may check your work on this part or Part 1. **DO NOT GO ON TO THE NEXT PART.**

STOP

7

PART 1

1. (A) (B) (C) (D)

2. (A) (B) (C) (D)

3. (A) (B) (C) (D)

4. (A) (B) (C) (D)

5. (A) (B) (C) (D)

6. (A) (B) (C) (D)

7. (A) (B) (C) (D)

8. (A) (B) (C) (D)

9. (A) (B) (C) (D)

10. (A) (B) (C) (D)

11. (A) (B) (C) (D)

12. (A) (B) (C) (D)

13. (A) (B) (C) (D)

14. (A) (B) (C) (D)

15. (A) (B) (C) (D)

16. (A) (B) (C) (D)

17. (A) (B) (C) (D)

18. (A) (B) (C) (D)

19. (A) (B) (C) (D)

20. (A) (B) (C) (D)

21. (A) (B) (C) (D)

22.

3	5	2	
/	/	/	/
.	.	.	.
0	0	0	0
1	1	1	1
2	2	2	2
3	3	3	3
4	4	4	4
5	5	5	5
6	6	6	6
7	7	7	7
8	8	8	8
9	9	9	9

23.

1	0	2	4
/	/	/	/
.	.	.	.
0	0	0	0
1	1	1	1
2	2	2	2
3	3	3	3
4	4	4	4
5	5	5	5
6	6	6	6
7	7	7	7
8	8	8	8
9	9	9	9

PART 2

1.

2.

SCORING GUIDE 1:

3 Student gives explicit consideration of at least 3 time components (time to exit – approximately 1 hr, gas – approximately 5 to 10 min, and 25 min to location)—may include a fourth component—time for parking, walking, etc. (The response must reveal that computation or estimation of (1) how far the person can travel on the remaining fuel or (2) how much gas was needed for 50+ miles was performed reasonably.) **AND** indication that person will not be on time by 5 to 20 minutes or by different amount if reasonably justified or that person could be on time with reasonable justification.

2 Student takes into account (at least implicitly) at least 3 time components with minor computational/estimation errors **AND** response regarding lateness (if and how much) consistent with the estimates given.

1 Student makes major error in computation/estimation of, or omission of, one time component **OR** response about lateness inconsistent with computations/estimations.

0 Blank or irrelevant or other incorrect response given.

SCORING GUIDE 2:

3 Student presents correct sketch with all pieces shown (labels are not required since they were on the pieces) **AND** correct expressions for the perimeter—$4(x + 1)$ or $4x + 4$ or equivalent—and for area—$(x + 1)^2$ or $x^2 + 2x + 1$ or $x^2 + x + x + 1$ equivalent.

2 Student presents correct sketch with correct expression for perimeter **OR** area, but not both **OR** correct expressions for both with no sketch or incorrect sketch.

1 Student presents correct sketch with incorrect or missing expressions for both perimeter and area **OR** missing or incorrect sketch with correct expression for either perimeter or area, but not both.

0 Blank paper or irrelevant or other incorrect response given.

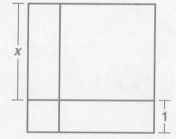 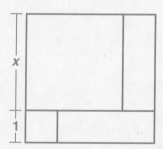

MATHEMATICS REFERENCE SHEET

Examples for Grid Responses

These are examples of how your answers should look. In each example, the appropriate circle in each column below each box with a number or symbol is completely darkened.

This grid has been filled in to show the answer one-half as a fraction. The one is in the first box, the fraction bar is in the second box, and the two is in the third box.

This grid has been filled in to show the answer one-half as a decimal number.

$\pi = 3.14$ or $3\frac{1}{7}$

2 cups = 1 pint

2 pints = 1 quart

4 quarts = 1 gallon

1 liter = 0.91 quarts

1 ton = 2,000 pounds

1 kilogram = 2.2 pounds

1 mile = 5,280 feet

1 inch = 2.54 centimeters

You may cut out the shapes below to use on the Sample Tests.

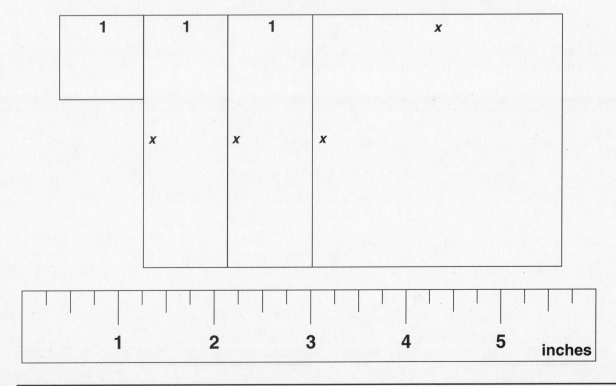

Circle

Area = πr^2
Circumference = $2\pi r$

Rectangle

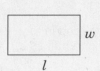

Area = lw
Perimeter = $(l + w)$

Parallelogram

Area = bh

Rhombus

Area = bh

Trapezoid

Area = $\frac{1}{2}(b_1 + b_2)h$

Triangle

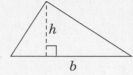

Area = $\frac{1}{2}bh$

Pythagorean Formula:

$c^2 = a^2 + b^2$

Rectangular parallelepiped

Volume = lwh

Sphere

Volume = $\frac{4}{3}\pi r^3$

Cone

Volume = $\frac{1}{3}\pi r^2 h$

Cylinder

Volume = $\pi r^2 h$

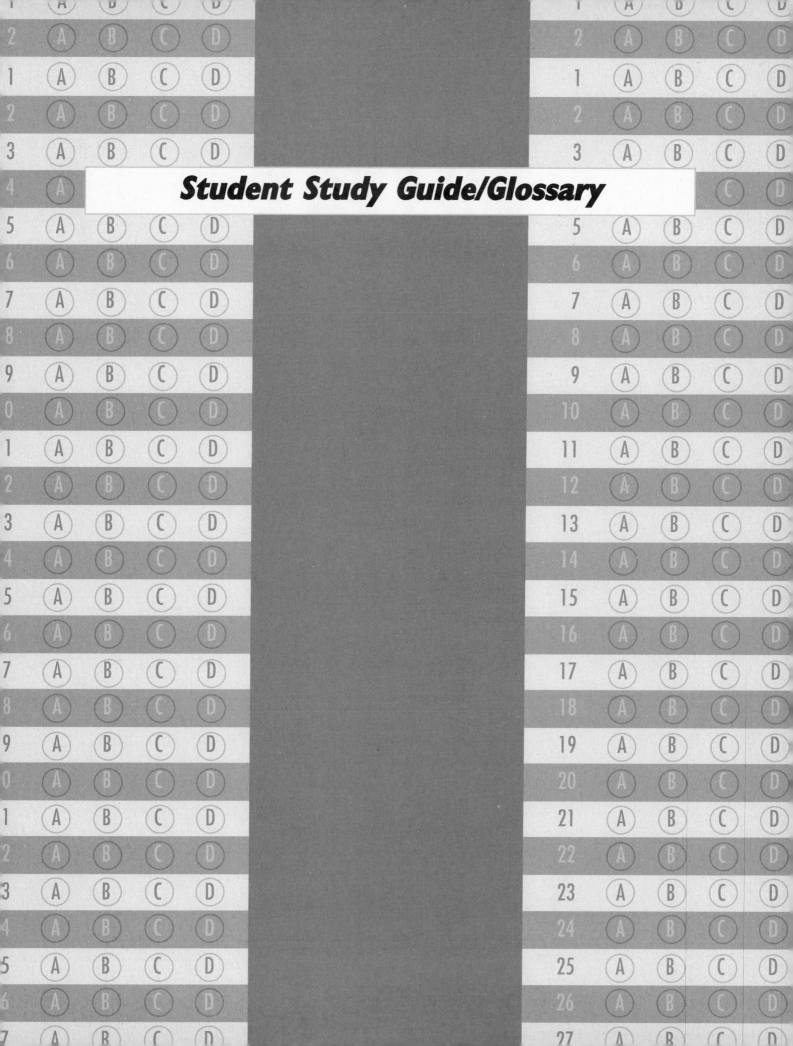

Student Study Guide/Glossary

A

Absolute value (p. 77)   A number's distance from zero on the number line is called its absolute value.

     Example   The absolute value of -3 is 3 because 3 is 3 units from zero on the number line.

Acute triangle (p. 50)   An acute triangle has three angles that measure less than 90°.

     Example $m\angle 1, m\angle 2, m\angle 3 < 90°$

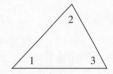

Area (pp. 58, 65)   Area is the number of square units needed to cover a figure.

     Example   The area of a circle is πr^2.

                    The area of a rectangle is $l \cdot w$.

                    The area of a triangle is $\frac{1}{2}bh$.

B

Bar graph (p. 125)   A bar graph compares amounts.

     Example   This bar graph represents class sizes for grades 6, 7, and 8.

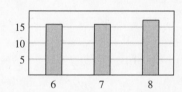

Base (p. 14)   When a number is written in exponential form, the number that is used as a factor is the base.

     Example $5^4 = 5 \times 5 \times 5 \times 5$

Bisector of a segment (p. 54)   The bisector of a segment divides the segment into two congruent segments.

     Example $\overline{GM} \cong \overline{MH}$. Line l is the bisector of segment GH.

C

Center of rotation (p. 86)   The point about which a figure is turned is the center of rotation.

Example   The origin is the center of this rotation.

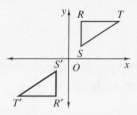

Circle (p. 58)   A circle is a set of points in a plane that are the same distance from a given point, called the center.

Example   Circle *O*

Circle graph (p. 129)   A circle graph displays data that represent parts of a whole.

Example   This circle graph represents the different types of plays William Shakespeare wrote.

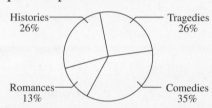

Circumference (p. 58)   Circumference is the distance around a circle. You calculate the circumference of a circle by multiplying the diameter by pi ($\pi \approx 3.14$).

Example   The circumference of a circle with a diameter of 10 cm is approximately 31.4 cm.

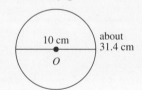

Cone (p. 104)   A cone is a space figure with one circular base and one vertex.

Example

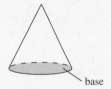

Congruent triangles (p. 51)   Triangles that have the same size and shape are congruent.

Example $AB = QS$, $CB = RS$, and $AC = QR$.
$m\angle A = m\angle Q$, $m\angle C = m\angle R$, and
$m\angle B = m\angle S$. Triangles ABC and QSR
are congruent.

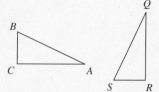

Coordinate (p. 41)   A coordinate is a number that corresponds to a point on a number line.

Example   The coordinate of K is 2.

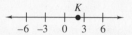

Coordinate plane (p. 78)   A coordinate plane is formed by the intersection of a horizontal number line called the x-axis and a vertical number line called the y-axis.

Example

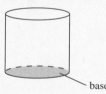

Cylinder (p. 104)   A cylinder is a space figure with two circular, parallel, and congruent bases.

Example

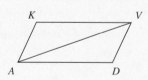

D

Diagonal of a quadrilateral (p. 54)   A diagonal of a quadrilateral is a segment that joins two nonconsecutive vertices.

Example $\overline{AV}$ is a diagonal of $KVDA$.

Diameter (p. 58)   A diameter is a segment that passes through the center of a circle and has both endpoints on the circle.

Example $\overline{RS}$ is a diameter of a circle O.

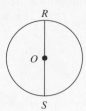

E

Equation (p. 161)   A mathematical sentence that contains an equal sign ($=$) is an equation.

Example $2(6 + 17) = 46$

Equilateral triangle (p. 50)   An equilateral triangle is a triangle with three congruent sides.

Example $\overline{SL} \cong \overline{LW} \cong \overline{WS}$

Exponent (p. 14)   An exponent expresses how many times a base is used as a factor.

Example $3^4 = 3 \times 3 \times 3 \times 3$

F

Factor (p. 17)   One number is a factor of another if it divides that number with no remainder.

Example   1, 2, 3, 4, 6, 9, 12, and 36 are factors of 36.

Fractal (p. 100)   A fractal is a geometric figure that is self-similar. At each stage each part of the figure is similar to the whole figure.

Example   Snowflake and fern patterns are examples of fractals found in nature.

H

Hypotenuse (p. 92)   The hypotenuse is the longest side of a right triangle. It is the side opposite the right angle.

Example $\overline{AC}$ is the hypotenuse of $\triangle ABC$.

I

Image (p. 86)

A point, line, or figure that has been transformed to a new set of coordinates is the image of the original point, line, or figure.

Example $A'\,B'\,C'\,D'$ is the image of $ABCD$.

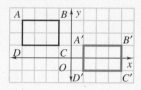

Inequality (p. 162)

An inequality is a relationship that compares two expressions.

Example $9 > y$

Isosceles triangle (p. 50)

An isosceles triangle is a triangle with at least two congruent sides.

Example $\overline{LM} \cong \overline{LR}$.

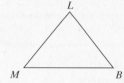

L

Least common multiple (p. 17)

The smallest number that is a common multiple of two or more numbers is the least common multiple.

Example The LCM of 15 and 6 is 30.

Legs of a right triangle (p. 92)

The two shorter sides of a right triangle form a right angle and are called the legs of the triangle.

Example $\overline{AB}$ and $\overline{AC}$ are the legs of $\triangle ABC$.

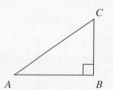

Line of symmetry (p. 81)

The line of symmetry is the line over which a figure is reflected.

Example Line l is a line of symmetry.

Linear relationship (p. 20)

Two variables have a linear relationship if it can be written in the form $y = mx + b$ where m and b are real numbers.

Example $y = 3x + 7$

Mean (p. 117)

The mean is the average value of a set, and is the sum of all the values divided by the number of values.

Example The mean temperature (° F) for the set of temperatures 44, 50, 48, 55, 60, 67, and 58 is: $\frac{44 + 52 + 48 + 55 + 60 + 67 + 58}{7} \approx 54.86°F$

Median (p. 117)

The median is the middle value in a set of data when the values are arranged in numerical order. If there is an even number of data items, add the middle two values and divide by two.

Example Temperatures (°F) for one week arranged in numerical order are 44, 48, 53, 55, 58, 60, and 67. 55 is the median because it is the middle number in the set of data.

Mode (p. 117)

The mode is the data item that occurs most frequently in a set of data.

Example The mode of the set of wages $2.75, $3.75, $3.60, $2.75, $3.70, is $2.75.

Multiple (p. 17)

A multiple of a number is the product of that number and any nonzero whole number.

Example Multiples of 13 are 13, 26, 39, 52, and so on.

O

Obtuse triangle (p. 50)

A triangle that contains one angle whose measure is greater than 90° and less than 180° is an obtuse triangle.

Example $90° < m\angle J < 180°$

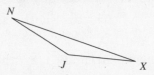

Opposite angles of a quadrilateral (p. 54)

Two angles of a quadrilateral that do not have a common side are opposite angles.

Example $\angle R$ and $\angle W$ are opposite angles of $RSWH$.

Opposite sides of a quadrilateral (p. 54)

Two sides of a quadrilateral that do not meet in an angle are opposite sides.

Example $\overline{RS}$ and $\overline{HW}$ are opposite sides of $RSWH$.

Order of operations (p. 153)   **1.** Do all operations within parentheses. **2.** Do all work with exponents. **3.** Multiply and divide from left to right. **4.** Add and subtract from left to right.

Example $2^3 (7 - 4) = 2^3 \cdot 3 = 8 \cdot 3 = 24$

Ordered pair (p. 78)   An ordered pair is a pair of numbers that describes the location of a point on a coordinate plane. The first value is the x-coordinate, and the second value is the y-coordinate.

Example $(-2, 1)$ is an ordered pair. The x-coordinate is -2; the y-coordinate is 1.

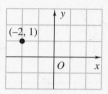

Origin (p. 80)   The origin is the intersection point of the x- and y-axes on a coordinate plane.

Example   The ordered pair that describes the origin is $(0, 0)$.

Outlier (p. 117)   A data item that is much higher or lower than the rest of the data is an outlier.

Example   An outlier in the list 6, 7, 9, 10, 11, 12, 14, 52, is 52.

 P

Parallel lines (p. 54)   Parallel lines are lines in the same plane that do not intersect.

Example $\overline{EF} \parallel \overline{HI}$

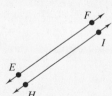

Parallelogram (p. 54)   A parallelogram has both pairs of opposite sides parallel.

Example $\overline{KV}$ is parallel to $\overline{AD}$, and $\overline{AK}$ is parallel to $\overline{DV}$, so *KVDA* is a parallelogram.

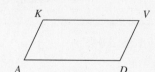

Perimeter (p. 69)

Perimeter is the distance around a figure.

Example The perimeter of rectangle $ABCD$ is 12 ft.

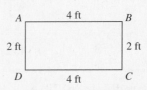

Perpendicular lines (p. 54)

Perpendicular lines are lines that intersect to form right angles.

Example $\overline{DE} \perp \overline{RS}$

Power (p. 14)

A number that is expressed using an exponent is called a power.

Example 2^4 is two to the fourth power; $2^4 = 2 \times 2 \times 2 \times 2$

Prime number (p. 17)

A number greater than 1 that is only divisible by 1 and itself is a prime number.

Example 13 is a prime number because its only factors are 1 and 13.

Prism (p. 104)

A prism is a space figure with two parallel and congruent polygonal faces, called bases. A prism is named by the shape of its base.

Example

Rectangular   Triangular   Hexagonal

Probability (p. 132)

The probability of an event is a number describing the chance that event will occur.

Example The probability of getting a 4 on spinning the wheel is $\frac{1}{8}$.

Proportion (p. 47)

A proportion is an equation stating that two ratios are equal.

Example $\frac{3}{12} = \frac{12}{48}$ is a proportion.

Pyramid (p. 104)

A pyramid is a space figure with triangular sides and only one polygonal base. A pyramid is named by the shape of its base.

Example

Triangular   Rectangular

Pythagorean Theorem (p. 92)   In any right triangle the square of the length of the hypotenuse is equal to the sum of the squares of the lengths of the legs.

Example   The right triangle shown has legs 3 and 4 and hypotenuse 5: $3^2 + 4^2 = 5^2$

Q

Quadrant (p. 78)   A quadrant is a section of the coordinate plane. The x- and y-axes divide the coordinate plane into four quadrants.

Example

Quadrilateral (p. 54)   A closed figure with exactly four sides is a quadrilateral.

Example   Squares, trapezoids, and parallelograms are quadrilaterals.

R

Radius (p. 58)   A radius is a segment that has one endpoint at the center and the other endpoint on the circle.

Example $\overline{OA}$ is a radius of circle O.

Range (p. 117)   The range of a set of data is the difference between the greatest and least values of the set.

Example   The range of the data 1, 3, 4, 2, 6, 1, 3 is $6 - 1 = 5$.

Rate (p. 46)   A rate is a ratio that compare two quantities measured in different units.

Example   A student types a 1,100 word essay in 50 min. The student's typing rate is 1100 words per 50 min, or 22 words/min.

Ratio (p. 46)   A ratio is a comparison of two numbers by division.

Example $\frac{1}{7}$ is a ratio expressing the number of Fridays in a week.

Rectangle (p. 54)   A rectangle is a parallelogram with four right angles.

Example

Rectangular parallelepiped (p. 114)   A rectangular parallelepiped is a space figure with six faces that are parallelograms.

Example

Reflection (p. 81)   A reflection flips a figure over a line.

Example $K' L' M' N'$ is a reflection of $KLMN$ over the y-axis.

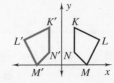

Repetend (p. 1)   A repetend of a pattern is a group of symbols that repeats in that pattern.

Example The repetend in the pattern WONKAWONKAWONK . . . is WONKA.

Rhombus (p. 54)   A rhombus is a parallelogram with four congruent sides.

Example

Right triangle (p. 50)   A right triangle is a triangle with one angle that measures 90°.

Example $m\angle B = 90°$.

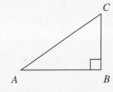

Rotation (p. 86)   A rotation turns a figure about a fixed point, called the center of rotation.

Example The image of $\triangle STR$ after a 180° rotation about the origin is $\triangle S'T'R'$. The origin is the center of rotation.

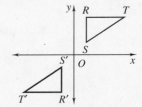

S

Scalene triangle (p. 50)   A scalene triangle is a triangle with no congruent sides.

       Example
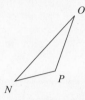

Self-similar figures (p. 100)   Each part of a self-similar figure is similar at each stage to the whole figure.

       Example
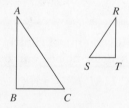

Sequence (p. 11)   A sequence is a set of numbers arranged according to a pattern.

       Example   3, 6, 9, 12, 15 is a sequence.

Similar triangles (p. 51)   Triangles that have the same shape but not necessarily the same size are similar.

       Example $\triangle ABC \sim \triangle RTS$
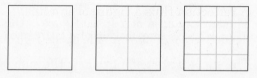

Space figures (p. 104)   Figures that do not lie in the plane are space figures.

       Example   Cylinders, spheres, pyramids, and prisms are space figures.

Sphere (p. 104)   A sphere is the set of all points in space that are the same distance from a given point called the center.

       Example

Square (p. 54)

A square is a parallelogram with four right angles and four congruent sides.

Example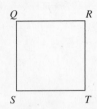

Square root (p. 93)

The opposite of squaring a number is finding its square root. The symbol for square root is $\sqrt{}$.

Example $\sqrt{25} = 5$ because $5^2 = 25$.

Surface area (p. 105)

The surface area of a space figure is the number of square units needed to cover the outside of the figure.

Example The surface area of a prism is the sum of the areas of the faces.

$4 \times 12 + 2 \times 9 = 66$ in.^{2} Each square = 1 in.^{2}

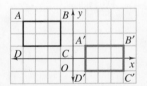

T

Transformations (p. 81)

Movements of figures on a plane are transformations. A transformation can be a translation, a reflection, or a rotation.

Example $K'\,L'\,M'\,N'$ is a reflection of $KLMN$ over the y-axis.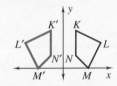

Translation (p. 82)

A translation slides a figure.

Example $ABCD$ has been translated to $A'\,B'\,C'\,D'$.

Trapezoid (p. 91)

A trapezoid has exactly one pair of parallel sides.

Example $UVYW$ is a trapezoid.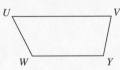

© Prentice-Hall, Inc.

Volume (p. 108)

The volume of a space figure is the number of cubic units needed to fill the space inside the figure.

Example The volume of the rectangular prism is 36 in.^{3}.

each cube = 1 in.^{3}

Acknowledgments

The following were picked up directly from HSPT Form 1, December 1990:

Chapter 1: p. 18, ex. 4; p. 36, ex. 4; p. 37, ex. 6
Chapter 2: p. 57, ex. 14; p. 64, ex. 16
Chapter 4: p. 120, ex. 14; p. 137, ex. 11; p. 142, example 1; p. 149, ex. 6
Chapter 5: p. 164, ex. 10; p. 172, ex. 8; p. 189, ex. 17

The following were picked up directly from HSPT Form 2, December 1990:

Chapter 1: p. 33, ex. 1; p. 38, ex. 14
Chapter 2: p. 45, ex. 21; p. 52, ex. 13; p. 60, ex. 17; p. 68, ex. 16; p. 74, ex. 17
Chapter 3: p. 107, ex. 8
Chapter 4: p. 134, ex. 8; pp. 138-139, ex. 1; p. 143, ex. 10; p. 147, ex. 6
Chapter 5: p. 168, ex. 14; p. 180, ex. 9; p. 186, ex. 5; p. 187, ex. 9; p. 188, ex. 14

The following were picked up directly from HSPT Form 3, December 1990:

Chapter 1: p. 37, ex. 9, 10
Chapter 2: p. 57, ex. 17; p. 72, ex 1; p. 73, ex. 10; p. 74, ex. 14
Chapter 4: p. 120, ex. 15; p. 133, example 2; p. 136, example 1; p. 150, ex. 9
Chapter 5: p. 164, ex. 11; p. 172, ex. 7; p. 177, ex. 16; p. 186, ex. 4; p. 187, ex. 11

The following were picked up directly from HSPT Form 1, December 1991:

Chapter 1: p. 38, ex. 12
Chapter 2: p. 47, example 1; p. 49, ex. 12; p. 53, ex. 16; p. 56, ex. 9; p. 72, ex. 4; p. 73, ex. 11
Chapter 4: p. 119, ex. 13; p. 120, ex. 16; p. 134, ex. 9; p. 151, ex. 11
Chapter 5: p. 169, ex. 20; p. 187, ex. 10; p. 188, ex. 12

The following were picked up directly from HSPT Form 2, December 1991:

Chapter 1: p. 36, ex. 5; p. 37, ex. 7
Chapter 2: p. 72, ex. 5
Chapter 3: p. 113, ex. 2
Chapter 4: p. 131, ex. 13; p. 144, ex. 1; p. 148, ex. 3
Chapter 5: p. 160, ex. 18; p. 172, ex. 10; p. 182, ex. 1; p. 186, ex. 3; p. 188, ex. 16

The following were picked up directly from HSPT Form 3, December 1991:

Chapter 1: p. 19, ex. 6; p. 39, ex. 16
Chapter 2: p. 49, ex. 9; p. 57, ex. 10; p. 72, ex. 6
Chapter 3: p. 114, ex. 5
Chapter 4: p. 119, ex. 12; p. 120, ex. 17; p. 123, ex. 7; p. 127, ex. 7; p. 150, ex. 8
Chapter 5: p. 163, ex. 6, 7; p. 172, ex. 9; p. 177, ex. 17; p. 186, ex. 7

HSPT Form 2, December 1991 is Sample Test 1.
HSPT Form 2, December 1990 is Sample Test 2.
HSPT Form 3, December 1990 is Sample Test 3.
HSPT Form 3, December 1991 is Sample Test 4.

The following were *adapted* from HSPT Form 1, December 1990:

Chapter 2: p. 48, ex. 8; p. 49, ex. 13; p. 68, ex. 14
Chapter 3: p. 106, ex. 6
Chapter 4: p. 118, ex. 10; p. 132, example 1
Chapter 5: p. 159, ex. 15; p. 187, ex. 8

The following were *adapted* from HSPT Form 2, December 1990:

Chapter 1: p. 27, ex. 14
Chapter 3: p. 80, ex. 12; p. 94, ex. 3; p. 95, ex. 10
Chapter 4: p. 125, ex. 1
Chapter 5: p. 161, example 2; p. 181, ex. 13

The following were *adapted* from HSPT Form 3, December 1990:

Chapter 1: p. 3, ex. 17
Chapter 2: p. 66, ex. 7-10
Chapter 3: p. 97, ex. 8; p. 98, ex. 12; p. 99, ex. 14; p. 103, ex. 14; p. 107, ex. 3; p. 113, ex. 3
Chapter 4: p. 138, example 1; p. 140, ex. 3
Chapter 5: p. 172, ex. 11

The following were *adapted* from HSPT Form 1, December 1991:

Chapter 1: p. 37, ex. 8
Chapter 2: p. 56, ex. 1-6
Chapter 3: p. 80, ex. 12; pp. 89-90, ex. 1-3
Chapter 4: p. 122, ex. 4; p. 124, ex. 8; p. 133, ex. 3; p. 140, ex. 4

The following were *adapted* from HSPT Form 2, December 1991:

Chapter 1: p. 18, example 3
Chapter 2: p. 45, ex. 23; p. 58, ex. 1-5
Chapter 3: p. 109, ex. 1
Chapter 4: p. 121, ex. 1-3
Chapter 5: p. 171, ex. 4; p. 176, ex. 14; p. 179, ex. 7

The following were *adapted* from HSPT, December 1992:

Chapter 1: p. 36, ex. 3
Chapter 2: p. 47, example 2; p. 74, ex. 15
Chapter 3: p. 83, ex. 8; p. 88, ex. 12; pp. 89-90, ex. 1-3; p. 108, ex. 11; p. 115, ex. 8
Chapter 4: p. 123, ex. 6; p. 138, example 1; p. 139, ex. 2; p. 140, ex. 3
Chapter 5: p. 160, ex. 17; p. 181, ex. 11; p. 185, ex. 8; p. 187, ex. 8